Royal Crown Derby
Paperweights

Royal Crown Derby
PAPERWEIGHTS

A Collectors' Guide
by Ian Cox
250th Anniversary Edition

ROYAL CROWN DERBY

194 Osmaston Road · Derby DE23 8JZ
ISBN I 85894 I2I O

Cover illustrations:
Front cover:
Garden Snail, Firecrest, Striped Dolphin
Front flap:
Millennium Bug
Back cover:
Dragon, Puffin, Bakewell Duck, Snake, Robin
Back flap:
Penguin and Chick, Teddy Bear, Koala and Baby,
Blue Tit, Humming Bird, Ladybird – Two-Spot

Frontispiece:
Deer, the first weight to be designed and manufactured
as an exclusive for members of the
Royal Crown Derby Collectors' Guild

First published 1997
Second revised and expanded edition 1998
Third edition revised and expanded by Sue Morecroft 2000

Photography by Mark Duckett ABIPP
at Nigel Taylor Photography
Original design by Dalrymple
Revised edition laid out and typeset in Caslon by Kate Ward
Produced by Merrell Publishers Limited
42 Southwark Street, London SEI IUN
Printed and bound in Italy

CONTENTS

Foreword

This is the third edition of Ian Cox's definitive work *Paperweights: A Collectors' Guide*. It has been a bible for collectors, not just for its practical lists, descriptions and illustrations, but also for its insight into the people and processes that lie behind these little works of art.

Over the centuries there have been many technical developments in our industry. We may be manufacturers of the traditional kind, but we have used the latest techniques in our design and production methods since 1750. Ian Cox's work brings out this point with great clarity.

This is a landmark edition for three reasons. The first is simply that there have been many additions and deletions to the paperweight range since the previous editions, so the book has been rearranged, re-photographed and brought completely up to date.

A second, more important, reason is that this edition is published in the 250th year since our predecessors started to produce porcelain in Derby. In the 1720s, Meissen discovered the secret of making articles successfully in a pure, white, vitrified body, as had been done for centuries in China. For decades they had kept the secret to themselves, but around 1745 a group of potters at the Chelsea factory worked out how it was done and started manufacture. They were closely followed by Planche and Duesbury at Derby, and by 1750 they, too, were in production, and heading for commercial and artistic success.

The third reason is that this edition is published shortly after Royal Crown Derby became, once again, an independent and freestanding company. On 1 July 2000 the company separated from its parent group, Royal Doulton, of which it had been a part since the early 1970s. In a sense, therefore, this edition is a celebration of our newly regained independence.

We have reason indeed to be proud of our 250-year heritage, which is one of continuous creativity. The paperweights are an example of this, part of a tradition that we trust will keep us in business for many years to come.

Hugh Gibson
Managing Director, Royal Crown Derby

opposite
Hugh Gibson with the Millennium Fountain, designed by John Ablitt and produced in 2000 to celebrate 250 years of china manufacture in Derby

CHAPTER I

Five Birds and a Rabbit

The birth of the Royal Crown Derby series of paperweights can be traced to a special event held at Chatsworth House in 1981, when, together with a number of new designs for tableware, the firm introduced six paperweights in animal form: an Owl, a Duck, a Quail, a Penguin, a Wren and a Rabbit. These new designs across the firm's whole product range signified Royal Crown Derby's commitment to the processes of renewal and innovation that are vital to all long-established companies if they are to develop new products suited to contemporary fashions and tastes. As its subsequent history proves, the paperweight range was an imaginative and well-conceived response to new challenges, and the first six weights provided the foundations for a remarkable success story for Royal Crown Derby.

The idea for the paperweight range can be directly attributed to Jo

The Royal Crown Derby factory at Osmaton Road, Derby

opposite
The first six Royal Crown Derby paperweights: Owl, Penguin, Wren, Duck, Quail, and Rabbit, introduced at Chatsworth house in 1981

Ledger, a talented and experienced designer and art director. Ledger had first become involved with Royal Crown Derby shortly after S. Pearson & Co., the parent firm of Allied English Potteries (the proprietor of the Derby factory at that time), acquired, in 1972, Royal Doulton. He became Art Director for the new Doulton Group, which now included Royal Crown Derby. While Royal Crown Derby retained its independent status as a pottery, with all processes continuing to take place in the factory on its Osmaston Road site, the implications for design activities were considerable. A spirit of close co-operation developed between the group's main design department at Nile Street in Stoke-on-Trent and the design department at Royal Crown Derby. Ledger visited the Derby factory on numerous occasions during the mid-1970s and made a notable input into the formulation of future production plans. After carefully studying the nature of contemporary Derby wares and after having had the opportunity to assess, first hand, the distinctiveness of the Royal Crown Derby factory and its special traditions, skills and ability to produce wares that would sell well in the prevailing market conditions, he was in a good position to make recommendations for new products. He believed that the time was right for Derby to diversify its product range further so as to embrace new ideas for giftwares which would be distinctively Derby in character, but new and fresh in concept and available to a wide range of potential customers.

THE PAPERWEIGHT CONCEPT

Ledger conceived the paperweight range as a generic series of useful but at the same time aesthetically attractive objects that would have broad appeal. Paperweights, which had first been widely manufactured in glass in the 1840s, were a type of object for which there was no strong ceramic tradition, presumably because of the fragility of ceramic bodies. Despite the potential problem of fragility, Ledger believed that there was an excellent opportunity to develop a range of ceramic paperweights that would be both novel in character and unique to Royal Crown Derby. Having made the decision to develop a series of paperweights, he was left with the question of what form they should take. After spending much time considering the characteristics and popularity of historical and contemporary wares from a range of English and European manufacturers, as well as from Derby, he reached the firm opinion that animal sculptures, which were always appealing to customers, and for which there was a Derby tradition, would make a fine theme for the new range. He also knew it was essential that the new range should specifically draw upon the traditions bound up with the highly significant history of pottery-making in Derby. The hallmarks of the range were to be a stylishness that would appeal to contemporary tastes and an appearance that would continue Derby traditions of rich decoration.

BUILDING ON TRADITIONS

In formulating ideas for the paperweight range, Jo Ledger had taken into account the fact that Derby manufactories had a strong tradition of making ceramic figures and toys that dated back to the establishment of a factory at Nottingham Road around 1750. A wide variety of animals and birds, including Boars, Lambs, Leopards and Canaries, had been skilfully modelled in soft-paste porcelain during the early 1750s; the Royal Crown Derby Museum has a fine example of a Charging Bull derived from a Meissen original, and Derby City Art Gallery and Museum holds an early example of a Derby Squirrel. Lambs and Sheep are also mentioned in the eighteenth-century Derby owner William Duesbury's London Account Book. The King Street factory, which was established in 1849, had also developed a tradition of making bone-china figures and animal models, a tradition that extended into the twentieth century and up to the date of the company's acquisition by Royal Crown Derby in 1935. At Osmaston Road, bone-china figures and animals have been made at the factory since the end of the nineteenth century; the Hunting Dogs made in the 1950s provide just one example of a series that brought the tradition of the highly skilled manufacture of animal models through to the modern period. In terms of subject-matter and craft skills, the new series of paperweights would be clearly rooted in traditions that went back to the very beginning of ceramic manufacture in Derby.

Squirrel, made at the Nottingham Road factory *c.* 1760. Now in the Derby Museum

Another important tradition to be absorbed into the design concept for the new paperweight range concerned the highly significant 'Imari' range of patterns developed in Derby factories from the late eighteenth century and again continuing through to the present day. These 'Imari' designs are based on Japanese porcelain wares decorated in underglaze blue, with overglaze iron red and gilding, and with patterns inspired by Japanese brocades; they are often also referred to as 'Japan' patterns. The wares were exported to the west via the port of Imari in the Arita province of Japan. They were popular in Europe during the early to mid-eighteenth century, at which time English porcelain manufacturers, too, began to introduce their own versions of Imari-inspired designs. Japan patterns were introduced at Derby early, and they have been a significant part of the production of the factories at Nottingham Road, King Street and Osmaston Road ever since. During the early nineteenth century Robert Bloor, proprietor of the Nottingham Road factory, capitalized on the popularity of Imari patterns by decorating large quantities of white ware with these rich designs, using the profits to finance new projects. Ceramic historians acknowledge that Derby factories made Imari-inspired designs their own, and indeed today, in the mind of the public, Imari-inspired wares are synonymous with Royal Crown Derby. The firm continues to manufacture tableware and giftware items using patterns based on the designs first developed at the Nottingham Road factory in the late eighteenth century. Pattern no. 1128, also known as 'Old Imari', is made today in the Royal Crown Derby factory basically to the design specifications laid down in a factory pattern-book of about 1880, which is now in the archive of the Royal Crown Derby Museum.

The value placed on the importance of this tradition in the paperweight formula is clearly discernible in a publicity brochure that accompanied the 1981 launch:

"These charming paperweights were modelled by internationally renowned sculptor Robert Jefferson and decorated by June and Brian Branscombe in a style so quintessentially Royal Crown Derby. Blue, red and gold are used in new pattern forms which draw their inspiration from Derby's long tradition of 'Imari' decorations."

TECHNICAL MATTERS

Following Royal Crown Derby's acquisition by Allied English Potteries in 1962, a management review of production methods at the Derby factory indicated that there were considerable advantages to be gained from developing new methods so as to improve efficiency in the factory's decorating shops, especially in those areas involving

below left
Hand-painted and gilded 'Imari' wares, produced prior to the introduction of lithograph technology in the 1960s and 1970s

below right
A range of Imari-inspired wares, decorated using lithograph technology

the manufacture of Imari-decorated wares. Brian Branscombe, the Derby Art Director, was given the task of coming up with some practical ideas for bringing this about. He had knowledge in depth of the nature and complexity of designs inspired by Japanese Imari patterns, but at the same time he was aware of the high production costs involved in making wares with complex patterns that had to be painted entirely by hand and fired at least four times. He recognized the need to develop mechanical methods for laying down such patterns as 'Old Imari' that would not, however, compromise the quality and appearance of the wares. Lithograph technology, involving the production of coloured transfers for application to ceramic bodies, was by this time being widely used in the Staffordshire Potteries, but it had been used only in a very limited way at Derby. The traditional Royal Crown Derby 'Posie' pattern was already being made on the basis of artwork developed in the Derby studio but with lithographs commissioned from an external source, but the Imari patterns were all still being hand-painted. It remained to be seen whether lithograph technology could be adapted to famous patterns such as 'Witches' and 'Old Imari'.

Avis Garton, present Head of the Technical Studio at Royal Crown Derby, joined the staff of the infant studio in 1965, along with her twin sister, May; both can remember Brian Branscombe carrying out homespun experiments with a primitive silkscreen made with the aid of parts taken from an old vacuum-cleaner. Branscombe's knowledge of silkscreening methods was at that time limited, so he took advice from as many people as possible, among whom his art-teacher sister proved to be a most useful source of information and ideas. Initial experiments involved developing silkscreen transfers for the in-glaze blue colours that were so much part of the Imari-inspired designs. They were successfully applied first to relatively simple flatware shapes. When this had been achieved, screens were developed to make transfers for the delicate, feathery, on-glaze iron-red patterns that filled the white-ground areas in the blue. Finally, the problem of the gold patterns that were superimposed over all the blue and red designs was vigorously attacked. Although progress was sometimes painfully slow, the results were impressive, and as the skills of the young technicians developed and their basic equipment was replaced with more efficient machinery, so the final product improved dramatically. Soon it even became possible to reproduce the gilders' 22-carat gold brushwork so exactly using the silkscreen method that only the trained eye could detect the difference between hand-painted and silkscreen-printed gilding.

Such developments were enthusiastically welcomed by the Derby management, and Branscombe and his wife, June, also a designer in the Derby Art Studio, working with the Garton twins, were given the task of perfecting the technique further and of gradually shifting a number of the traditional Derby Japan patterns over to this method of decoration. The process took several years to complete, and Avis Garton remembers that some of the Imari patterns were still being hand-painted and gilded in the decorating shops at the end of the 1970s. The remarkable end result of this ten-year development, however, was authentic Derby Japan patterns that had not had to be simplified with the introduction of new technology: the quality of the resulting products was excellent and yet the new processes had helped to improve efficiency – just what the factory management was looking for.

The movement over to lithograph decoration for a good number of the Imari-patterned wares had transformed the quality of these ranges and ensured their continued viability, which could not have been certain if they had continued to be entirely hand-painted, but what was the significance of these events for the development of the paperweight range? Ledger recognized that the staff working in the Technical Studio had become extraordinarily adept at solving the problem of adapting highly complex graphics with all-over patterns to the production of lithographs that could be applied over three-dimensional surfaces: here was a skills resource bank that had enormous potential in terms of product development. Ledger recognized that within the Derby factory there was an enormous battery of creative potential waiting to be tapped and channelled into the development of the new range.

BIRTH OF THE NEW RANGE

By the end of the 1970s the concept of the new paperweight range was fully formed. The hallmarks of the series, a stylish animal theme and richness of decoration, were to be coupled with the continuing use of Imari-inspired patterns, but in new and interesting ways. The weights were to be usable, and the sculptural forms of the animals were to capture essential characteristics of the chosen species, rather than being exact likenesses. It was essential that the proposed models should be capable of being translated into factory production using the recently established lithograph technology – the notion being to create products that were innovative, "essentially Derby in character" but also accessible to a wide range of potential customers.

Jo Ledger remembered that in the early 1970s he had commissioned a couple of animal sculptures with the idea of developing the product range at Royal Doulton's Crystal factory. The production team at the Tutbury works had, however, rejected these as being unsuitable for translation into a glass medium, and so they had sat on a shelf in the design studio, gathering dust. Ledger retrieved them and considered the possibilities of using them, or something similar, for the start of the new Derby range. The models had been sculpted by Robert Jefferson, a freelance sculptor of considerable ability who had previously worked for the Poole Pottery Studio in Dorset. Jo had already used Jefferson to produce some ideas for a series of birds that had gone into production at Nile Street, so now he asked Jefferson to come up with some ideas for the new Derby range. Prototype clay models were developed for the introductory range, and, when it had been agreed they met the criteria for the paperweight brief, they were put into trial production and bone-china versions of the sculptures were made. At this point the process used to develop paperweights involved a clear separation between sculpting and surface design, and Ledger asked Brian and June Branscombe to produce the designs for the decoration of the new models. Using the traditional Imari palette of colours – mazarine blue, iron red and gold – the Branscombes produced graphics for the models in line with the brief they had all agreed. The final stage of this process was the translation of the designs into workable production stages using the skills they had developed with the Garton twins in the Technical Studio. In late 1980 the first six models went into production, in time for the Chatsworth House launch in 1981. Although the event marked the official birth of the new series, they were given no more than half a page of coverage with a coloured illustration towards the back of the brochure designed to publicize the event. At that time no one could have guessed that the product range was not merely to become highly successful, but was also to help transform the overall prospects of the company in the 1990s.

Chatsworth House publicity brochure, illustrating the six original paperweights and some of the other products

CHAPTER 2

From Imari Frog to Garden Snail

Since the paperweight range was introduced in 1981, a gradual process of evolution has enhanced it beyond all expectations. New additions have been made to the list almost yearly so that over one hundred and fifty paperweights have been designed and produced since those early beginnings. Although nearly sixty of the designs from the 1980s and 1990s have now been withdrawn, or 'retired' as the firm prefers to call it, the number of paperweights in production is still in excess of fifty. How and precisely in what ways has the range changed since the first six were introduced in 1981? What factors have influenced the evolutionary process and affected such important matters as choice of subject and the aesthetic appearance of the weights, and how have these considerations been reflected in the models that have gone into production?

Statistical information concerning introduction dates provides a useful starting point for considering the growth of the paperweight series. Between 1981 and 2000 ninety paperweight models were introduced at an average rate of about five per year. The pattern has not, however, been consistent, and the illustrated graph shows that six introductions in the first year were followed by none in 1982, by six in 1983 and by none again in 1984. Between 1987 and 1991 there was a steady and consistent rise in the number of introductions, followed by a plateau of six a year for three years. An increase in introductions in 1995 and 1996 resulted in a second plateau of eleven weights per

Opposite
Paperweights on trolleys awaiting quality control at the factory

NUMBER OF PAPERWEIGHT INTRODUCTIONS BY YEAR
1981–2000

1981 1982 1983 1984 1985 1986 1987 1988 1989 1990 1991 1992 1993 1994 1995 1996 1997 1998 1999 2000

year for four years – and a further ten are planned for 2001. The pattern plotted here prompts some interesting questions about what lies behind the peaks and troughs at the beginning and the steady rise in the number of introductions in recent years.

In 1981, when the six original weights went into production, little attention was paid to sales prospects for the infant range and its future development, and no new models were planned for 1982 – certainly the management and Jo Ledger in the Design Studio had no grand plan waiting to be implemented. Despite the need for an early diversification of the Derby product range within this giftware

left to right
Duck, one of the six original weights introduced in 1981

Turtle, 1983

Walrus, 1987

Imari Frog, 1983

area, the early development of the series seems to have been tentative and very much 'toe in the water'. It is interesting that Ledger recalls the Derby Managing Director coming to him in the early 1980s, some time after the original launch, to ask what plans he had for new paperweights, a question prompted by the rising demand for the models already in production. Ledger remembers concocting some kind of positive response and then rushing off to talk with colleagues about the possibility of developing quickly ideas for some new subjects, together with related sculptures and artwork.

The process for introducing new models seems also to have been characterized by informality among the group of people involved. Ledger would come up with some ideas and discuss them with the sculptor Bob Jefferson, and prototypes would then be produced. Ledger would then take these to Brian and June Branscombe in the Design Studio, and they in turn would come up with proposals for decorating them. Nevertheless, close scrutiny of the original six weights shows that artistically and technically they satisfied the original design brief almost exactly.

The sculptural form of the early animals and birds was relatively simple, enough subtly to suggest the form or embrace the essential characteristics of a particular beast and yet at the same time make it appear attractive to hold, an important consideration given the function of the objects as paperweights. The models also succeeded, as they have continued to do ever since, in capturing aspects of behaviour reminiscent of the animals they represent – the quiet pose of a Duck at rest, the alert stance of the garden Wren and the arrogant posture of the emperor Penguin providing just a few examples of the variety to be found in the early group of weights. The artwork

produced for the surface decoration was never meant to be realistic, and the decision to signify Derby distinctiveness by restricting the colour range to the Imari colours of mazarine blue, iron red and gold made sure of that. The graphics, however, were always designed accurately to signify body features such as fur, feathers and scales or to incorporate motifs and patterns characteristic of a particular animal's form, behaviour or habitat. The decoration might be wholly in the Derby tradition, as in the case of the Turtle where the segments of the shell were filled with motifs directly taken from 'Old Imari' pattern no. 1128, or more abstract in character as in the case of the Walrus where the kaleidoscopic surface decoration contained motifs connected with the animal's marine habitat, including wave forms, sea anemones and starfish. The Imari Frog, introduced early in 1983, received, according to June Branscombe, a standing ovation when it was reviewed by the management before it went into full-scale factory production. The sculpture cleverly captured the pose of a frog squatting on a lily pad as if poised to leap into water; again the surface pattern found on the body was based on the rich Imari palette of colours, but this time the motifs were suggestive of the scaly, textured surface of an amphibian's skin. Not all of the designs were successful pieces of sculpture, it has to be said. One can see why the Owl, first produced in 1981, was modelled in an inclined position, as it paid homage to its paperweight function and made it easier to hold. The design was in fact based loosely on a terracotta owl originating from Corinth in the seventh century BC. The original, however, had been bent over, tearing the flesh of captive prey, a subject thought to be inappropriate for the paperweight model. The resulting sculpture did not quite succeed in capturing the essence of the 'wise' old owl and it looked a bit as though it had leaned too far over!

During the mid-1980s, as paperweight sales began gradually to rise, the informal design processes that characterized the approach used to develop new models gathered pace and a number of creative ideas involving modelling and graphics were tried out. The continuing separation between the design activities and crafting of the sculptures and the production of the surface decoration of the new models guaranteed the creation of an interesting and diverse group of subjects.

In the first instance, the weights were all of a muchness in terms of size – large enough to be held in the palm of the average adult hand. There were a couple of exceptions, such as the Wren and the Rabbit, which were smaller than the models so far mentioned, but there were no large examples initially. The first larger-scale model to be introduced was the Ram, which was designed and put into production in 1989, by which time the series was well established. Despite its higher cost, the model sold well, demonstrating that collectors were prepared to accept and to purchase more expensive weights. The way was open for the development of a range of larger models, including Large Elephant (1990), Bald Eagle (1992), Bengal Tiger (1994), Zebra (1995), Lion (1996), Camel (1996) and the Lady Amherst and Golden Pheasants (2000). At about the same time it was realized that the miniature sizes were also going to be popular, by virtue of their relative cheapness and also because they appeared cute to customers. Introductions in the small-size category have included Blue Tit (1994), Two-Spot Ladybird (1997), Swimming Duckling (1998), Sleeping Piglet (1999) and Firecrest (2000). Diversification in size has shown that there is room in the market for high-volume/low-profit models as well as for the more expensive low-volume/high-profit versions. The success of the former has allowed the development of the latter – enhancing choice for the collector, but also providing motivation and artistic stimulus for the designers working in

opposite Camel, introduced in 1996

the Art Department at Royal Crown Derby. Diversification in terms of size, however, has not been the only way in which the range has evolved.

New models have also been developed on the theme of the family related to a successful existing weight: for example, a Baby Rabbit was introduced in 1990 to complement the early Rabbit (1981), and Sheep (1991), Lamb (1992) and Twin Lambs (1993) developed the popular theme that had started with Ram in 1989. Another group of paperweights based round a particular animal that has proved to be successful in terms of the generation of ideas for new models has been that of cats. It started with a single Cat in 1985. Since then there has been a Kitten (1990), a Ginger Cat (1990), a Sleeping Kitten (1991), a Playful Kitten (1993), a Grey Kitten (1995), a Contented Cat (1995), a Contented Kitten (1996), a Siamese Cat and Siamese Kitten (both 1996), a Catnip Kitten (1997), a Majestic Cat (1997) and a Ginger Kitten (2000).

An expansion to cover different types of terrestrial and marine

right
Cat, Kitten, Sleeping Kitten, Playful Kitten

opposite
Majestic Cat, Grey Kitten, Ginger Cat, Ginger Kitten and Catnip Kitten

Farmyard habitat group:
Cockerel, Nanny Goat, Lamb,
Chicken, Swimming Duckling,
Sitting Duckling and Sleeping
Piglet

habitats has also characterized the evolution of the range. Themes related to the countryside (Rabbit, Owl, Red Squirrel, Red Fox, Dappled Quail, Country Mouse), the garden (Wren, Robin, Chaffinch, Blue Tit), ponds, streams and rivers (Frog, Kingfisher, Swan, Coot, Mallard Duck), the seashore and sea (Walrus, Puffin, Striped Dolphin, Seahorse, Penguin and Chick), the farmyard (Lamb, Cockerel, Chicken, Sleeping and Sitting Piglets, Swimming and Sitting Ducklings, Nanny Goat) and wild animals (Bengal Tiger, Bengal Tiger Cub, Lion, Zebra, Savannah Leopard) have all provided rich inspiration for the designers. Other interesting themes have included the introduction of weights connected with Chinese New Years, including Dragon (1988), Horse (1990) and Monkey and Baby (1992). Paperweights with a national theme have also been tried. The Koala and the Platypus were introduced in 1988 to celebrate the Australian bicentenary. The Bald Eagle (1992) was first produced for the American market and three weights were requested by Canada: the Chipmunk (1986), Beaver (1994) and Blue Jay (1995), the last associated with the Toronto 'Blue Jays' baseball team. The latest national paperweights are The Australian Collection, a trio of weights launched in advance of the Olympics, having gold back-stamps and certificates until the end of 2000.

The development of the paperweight range has not been led exclusively by artistic decisions taken within the confines of the Design Studio, for, since the bottom line for any business is steady growth and continuing profitability, artistic and aesthetic development of the series must be seen within this broad, overall context. In fact the interplay between economic considerations and artistic ideas within the factory makes for an interesting insight into the way Royal Crown Derby operates as a dynamic, modern business.

It has already been noted that the early series started to perform well in the mid-1980s, when production volumes began to rise in response to increased consumer demand. A report commissioned by the management to assess the performance of the paperweights for the period 1985–90 provided valuable data for developing ideas about the way the range should develop in the 1990s and beyond. There were many signs that the paperweight products were indeed performing well. In 1990 Royal Crown Derby had sold over three quarters of a million paperweights, and by the end of 1999 this figure had risen to nearly one and a half million. Further investigation of sales figures showed that in the late 1980s demand for paperweights within the United Kingdom accounted for more than eighty per cent of all the orders taken, and this had increased to eighty-nine per cent in 1999.

Seashore habitat paperweight:
Striped Dolphin

below left
The Australian Collection, 1999:
Koala and Baby, Kangaroo and
Duck-billed Platypus

below right
Chinese New Year group: Dragon,
Horse, and Monkey and Baby

27

The statistical information contained in the report also showed that the series was developing dynamically with a good interaction between the creative development of the product range and customer demand for different models. During the period 1985–90, when the number of models in production increased from sixteen to thirty-six, demand patterns reveal considerable interest in the new additions to the range. For example, the nine new models introduced in 1990 accounted for thirty-five per cent of sales by volume and forty per cent by value. Figures also showed that increases in turnover were due at least in part to the sale of the more expensive weights and not just to an increase in the volume of the number of pieces sold. This was tangible confirmation that collectors were prepared to pay more for the larger models that were beginning to be introduced. Additional research showed that the range did not in fact appear to be over price-sensitive and that the nature and characteristics of a model were far more important considerations than price alone. Models that appealed to customers, especially new ones, sold well at a rate independent of their retail price. Sales figures also showed that new models often achieved 'top ten' status within a year of introduction. Analysis of sales data for individual paperweights showed that the best performers had the following characteristics: their subject was easily recognizable, they were richly decorated, they were aesthetically pleasing and they were charming in character. Poorer performers tended to have simple decoration, with a high degree of white showing on the body of the paperweight, or were little-known subjects.

The production of this report had significant repercussions for the development of the paperweight range. First, the findings provided a tremendous boost to the confidence of all those involved in managing the development of the series. The policy of developing new models annually and diversifying the range in terms of size and subject-matter was paying off, and the new design conceptions were proving on the whole to be attractive to consumers. Consumers were prepared to pay more for the larger, richly decorated weights, such as the Large Elephant, further stimulating management to continue with this approach. The notion of giving the paperweights Derby distinctiveness by using the Imari palette in new and interesting ways was proving to be very appealing. But what could they do next? How was the Derby management to develop further the very successful formula that had come about largely as a result of a process of trial and error and pragmatic decision-making? The answer came in the form of two different but interrelated courses of action that were underpinned by the findings contained in the research document.

opposite
Large Elephant, introduced in 1990

Squirrel, introduced in 1991

Partridge, introduced in 1999

opposite A selection of Sue Rowe's designs: Dragon of Happiness, Old Imari Honey Bear, Rowsley Rabbit, Baby Rowsley Rabbit, Firecrest and Bluebird

One pathway has been largely design-led, inspired by the knowledge that economically the results had a good chance of success. The other course of action has been market-led, but has had considerable implications for work in the Design Studio.

The design-led pathway has been characterized by allowing the informal processes for developing new models, which had built up naturally over a period of time, to continue. Ideas for new paperweights originate from a whole variety of sources to the extent that anyone in the Royal Crown Derby workforce can nominate a suggestion for the list of paperweight proposals. Joyce Fletcher, for example, a former receptionist at Royal Crown Derby, wanted a squirrel added to the series; the suggestion was thought to be a good one so ideas for a squirrel were developed. A couple of times each year a meeting involving the Managing Director, the Sales and Marketing Director and the Design Director carefully considers new suggestions, and the designers themselves are often brought into the discussions. Louise Adams, the Art Director at Royal Crown Derby, consciously supports the notion of a number of individuals being involved in the development of the paperweights, and the manage-ment support the idea that no single aesthetic or 'look' should dominate the character, appearance and further development of the series as a whole. In the early days the range was overseen by Jo Ledger, the Doulton Art Director, working in association with the sculptor Bob Jefferson and the Derby Art Director, Brian Branscombe, and his wife, June. Following Brian's premature death in 1988 and the retirement of Jo Ledger and Bob Jefferson a few years later, a significant development has been the enhancement of the Royal Crown Derby Design Studio with the appointment of new full-time designers and the commissioning of paperweights from a number of outside designers as well. As new designers have been introduced, so they have been given the opportunity to express their own ideas as proposals for new weights have been developed.

Sue Rowe, a senior designer at Royal Crown Derby, has worked extensively for the last thirteen years developing Imari-inspired designs for Derby tableware and giftware ranges. Over the last four years she has also been involved in producing designs for a number of paperweights. She has been particularly involved in the transfer of the 'Old Imari' pattern on to paperweight shapes (Piglet, 1996; Old Imari Honey Bear, 1997; Polar Bear, 1998; Rocky Montain Bear and Old Imari Frog, 1999). Her designs for the Siamese Cat and Kitten (both 1996) are inspired by colourful Paisley patterns that show her individual approach and her extensive knowledge of the Derby Imari

tradition. Sue has designed a number of exclusively commissioned pieces that include the Mulberry Hall Frog (1996), Rowsley Rabbit (1997) and Baby Rowsley Rabbit (2000), Imperial Panda (1998), Leicestershire Fox (1999), the Dragon of Happiness (1999) and the Dragon of Good Fortune (2000). Sue has also contributed to the success of the Royal Crown Derby Guild with her designs for complimentary and exclusive Guild pieces (these include Mole, 1995; Poppy Mouse, 1996; Derby Wren, 1998; and Firecrest, 2000).

Louise Adams, the Art Director at Royal Crown Derby, has designed six new paperweights. The tortoiseshell Catnip Kitten was the Guild complimentary piece in 1995, and this was followed by three exclusive designs (Mulberry Hall Large Elephant, 1997; Mulberry Hall Baby Elephant, 1998; and the Unicorn, 1999). The Woodland Pheasant and Dappled Quail were both launched in 1999.

Tien Manh Dinh is a relatively new designer at Royal Crown Derby. He has successfully designed accent plates and miniature giftware, and has recently become involved in designing paperweights. The first design proved very popular with Guild members; this was the complimentary Meadow Rabbit. A further three designs all made their debut in 2000. The Garden Snail is the 2000 Event piece, and two exclusive weights are the Madagascan Tortoise for Sinclairs and Nanny Goat for the Royal Crown Derby Visitor Centre.

June Branscombe has been a designer at Royal Crown Derby for over thirty years and has been involved in all aspects of tableware and giftware design. She is an expert on heraldry and all things royal, and has designed most of the royal commemoratives in recent years. The first paperweight designed by June was the Ram in 1989, followed by the Seahorse and Sheep in 1991, the Lamb in 1992, Twin Lambs in 1993 and the Dove of Peace in 1995. For 2000 June has designed two very different pieces: the Heraldic Crown, celebrating the 100th year of Her Majesty Queen Elizabeth the Queen Mother, and the Computer Mouse decorated with printed circuits, pixels and cursors.

Yet another approach has been taken by Derby designer John Ablitt. Ablitt produced designs for Royal Doulton and Minton under the direction of Jo Ledger during the 1980s but did not become involved with Royal Crown Derby paperweights until the early 1990s, when he was asked to produce designs for a Hummingbird paperweight that went into production in 1993. Since then he has produced many successful designs, including Deer (1994), Zebra (1995), Teddy Bear (1997), Little Owl (1998) and Lady Amherst Pheasant and Golden Pheasant (2000). Ablitt continues the tradition of working informally with the team at the factory and he makes

Dappled Quail, introduced in 2000

Madagascan Tortoise, introduced in 2000

opposite
A selection of John Ablitt's designs: Drummer Bear, Barn Owl, Santa and Sleigh, Mallard Duck, Derby Ram, Millennium Bug and Nuthatch

regular visits to liaise closely with the Art Director and Design Studio. He has, however, taken responsibility for producing both the sculptural models and the graphics for his paperweights. Several years ago Jo Ledger came up with the idea of sitting paperweights on defined bases to produce additional areas for graphic decoration, and John has since used modelled shapes with distinctive flat surfaces for graphic decoration. This enabled John to experiment with complex, original, repeating patterns inspired by the animal's habitat. This method is used to great effect on John's latest paperweight designs. These are the complementary Lady Amherst and Golden Pheasants, which have been launched in 2000 in celebration of 250 years of china manufacture in Derby. Both pheasants appear to be striding through ornate formal gardens of neat flower-beds, clipped hedgerows, edged pathways and ornate urns. The semicircular design running around the bases of each weight is inspired by the metal crown that adorns the roof of the Royal Crown Derby factory. John has successfully integrated the true colours of the pheasants with the rich and traditional Imari colours.

John Ablitt's approach has, since 1993, taken one strand of the paperweight series in new directions, but his concentration on richness of decoration with an inclination to move away from the traditional

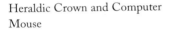

Heraldic Crown and Computer Mouse

palette of Imari colours was controversial in the first instance. The findings of the research report did, however, suggest that boldness would pay off, and it is refreshing to find that the management had the confidence to allow a new design-led strand of development to take root and grow. Many of John Ablitt's designs have been for large models and have had complicated graphics, which has resulted in a higher-than-average retail price. Again, however, the research report supported the notion of allowing the range to develop some models that fell into this category; the management could be sure that customers would buy the weights if they found them appealing.

The market-led development strategy is another facet of the paperweight story that has had a major impact on the evolution of the series since the publication of the research report in 1991, though it was to be a couple of years before the effect was fully felt. Simon Willis, the Sales and Marketing Director at Royal Crown Derby, believes that some of his colleagues were slow to recognize that the paperweight series was more than just a range of exclusive giftware objects and that individual paperweights were becoming highly collectable in their own right. Although the 1991 report was not a market research document as such, the results – above all the sales figures for the new models – strongly suggested that customers were collecting within the themes that were being established in the series. Information from other sources was also showing that a healthy market was beginning to establish itself for models that had been withdrawn from production. For the Seal, Hedgehog and Blue Fox, for example, which had all been withdrawn from production as early as 1987, second-hand values were rising as new collectors wanted to add these rare models to their holding of weights. How then could the Derby team use this information to help develop the range further?

The first withdrawals: Seal, Hedgehog and Blue Fox

At a basic level the management recognized that they must continue with the process of refreshing the range continually by adding new models every year. Indeed, the research report data provided the team with the confidence to increase the number of yearly additions, hence the steep rise in the graph showing paperweight introductions to approximately eleven models per year at the present time. The additions were not, however, to be all of the same kind. Some were to be at the medium and lower end of the price range and be mainstream production, others were to be of the larger and more expensive kind and yet others were to be issued on a more exclusive basis. At the same time it was important that the company kept a very watchful eye on the total number of weights in current production, as too

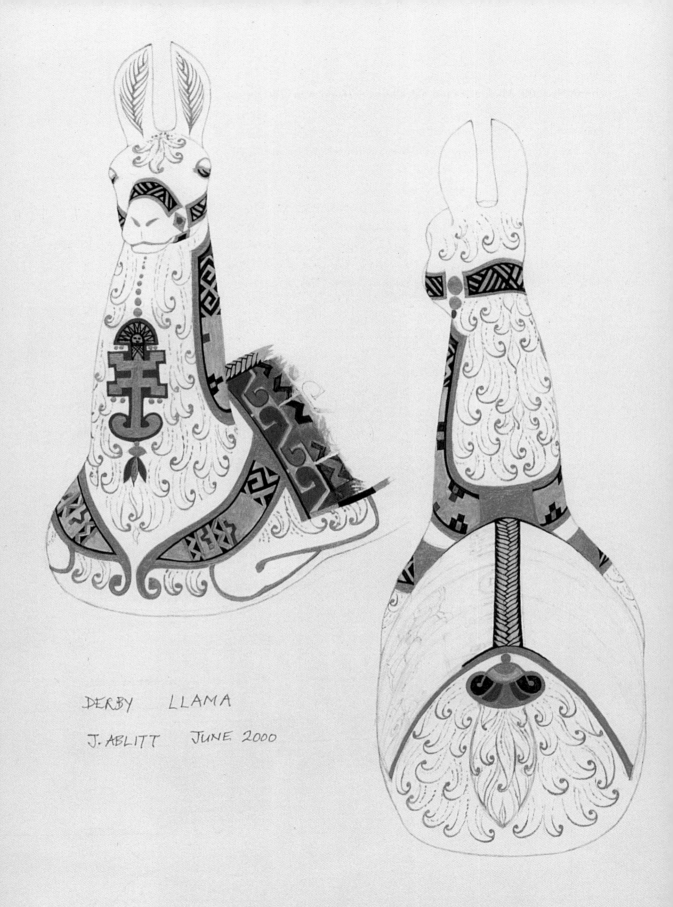

DERBY LLAMA

J. ABLITT   JUNE 2000

many items could stretch the resources of the moulding and decorating shops. Now the Marketing and Sales team draw up annually a list of paperweights that will be withdrawn the following year. This policy helps to control the total number of weights in production at any one time and it further helps to stimulate the collectable nature of the range. Full details of paperweights which have been withdrawn from production are given in Chapter Five.

Artwork of Puppy, Royal Crown Derby Collectors' Guild exclusive for 2001

A further consequence of the realization that the market had helped develop a significant collectable dimension to the paperweight range was the establishment of the Royal Crown Derby Collectors' Guild in 1994. The Guild was set up to provide collectors with up-to-date information about the paperweight range – details of new models, the work of new designers and interesting information about the background to new designs. At the same time, membership of the Guild was designed to confer special privileges on members in terms of what they could acquire. The Deer paperweight, designed by John Ablitt, was the first model produced exclusively for members of the Royal Crown Derby Collectors' Guild. Introduced early in 1994 at a retail price of £150, it was available to Guild members only until the end of that year; the model has a special backstop that reads *Designed Exclusively for The Royal Crown Derby Collectors' Guild*. Each year the factory has commissioned and produced a design exclusive to Guild members – the Mole (1995), Fawn (1996), Nesting Chaffinch (1997), Debonair Bear (1998), Woodland Pheasant (1999), Orchard Hedgehog (2000) and the Llama (for 2001). An annual complimentary paperweight is also available to new members as part of an introductory pack. The first complimentary weight was the Grey Kitten in 1995, followed by the Poppy Mouse (1996), Catnip Kitten (1997), Derby Wren (1998), Meadow Rabbit (1999), Firecrest (2000) and Puppy (for 2001). The Guild has been very successful and has built up a membership of more than 16,000 members since it was launched in 1994.

Increasing numbers of events were requested by retailers and it was decided that an annual limited-edition paperweight should be launched that would be available only at Royal Crown Derby events. The first piece was the Majestic Cat in 1997, followed by the Old Imari Frog (1998), Partridge (1999), Garden Snail (2000) and the Harbour Seal (for 2001).

The notion of producing exclusives has been further developed with pre-launch paperweights that are distributed through retail outlets that have traditionally sold Derby products. John Ablitt's Zebra, Camel and Lion were all pre-launched by Harrods and

opposite Artwork of Llama, Royal Crown Derby Collectors' Guild exclusive for 2001

included the Harrods logo within the designs. Connaught House pre-launched the Striped Dolphin in 1999, Geoff Taylor of Reigate the Bluebird in 2000, and Govier's of Sidmouth, which pre-launched the Old Imari Bears (Honey Bear, Polar Bear and Rocky Mountain Bear), will pre-launch the Donkey paperweight at the end of 2000.

A number of strictly limited-edition pieces have been commissioned. The first were Gumps Large Elephant (1990) and Bald Eagle (1992), followed by Small Elephant (1999). Wheelers commissioned the Dove in 1995 to mark the fiftieth anniversary of the end of World War II, and this was issued as an edition of 150. Sinclairs have commissioned two series of exclusively designed weights. The first series, launched between 1995 and 1997, has been succeeded by a new series of six endangered species. The first three weights in this second series were the Imperial Panda (1998), Savannah Leopard (1999), and Madagascan Tortoise (2000). Mulberry Hall of York have also commissioned numbered editions, including the Frog (1996), and the Large and Baby Elephants (1997 and 1998). Peter Jones commissioned the Dragon of Happiness (1999) and the Dragon of Good Fortune (2000) to celebrate 2000, the Year of the Dragon.

The selective design and production of exclusive paperweights has been a market-led initiative that has further fuelled and fired the development of the paperweight range in the last few years.

The exclusivity of the range has been further enhanced by the culmination of a unique and historic project initiated by Hugh Gibson's visit to Japan in 1998. Imaemon XIII, a Living National Treasure, holder of one of the highest honours in Japan, has personally created designs for the Imaemon Paperweight Collection. These ten paperweight models will be available in small limited editions in a choice of three colourways.

In a span of twenty years the Royal Crown Derby paperweight series has grown from humble beginnings – just six weights were produced in 1981 – to a situation where the production of the weights is now part of the essential lifeblood of the factory. Currently, thirty-nine per cent of factory production is concerned with paperweights, a figure that is set to increase as the range expands even further and new markets are tapped.

The Mulberry Hall Frog, introduced in 1996 as a limited edition

opposite
Some of the paperweights exclusive to selected retailers: Harrods Bald Eagle, Savannah Leopard, Striped Dolphin, Bakewell Duckling, Govier's Drummer Bear and Leicestershire Fox

39

wrong g. for head.   wrong g. for head.

DERBY MALLARD · PAPERWEIGHT
J. ABLITT APRIL '76

IN g.?

if tail is in glaze, will prob need extra black/brown on g. for back, beak + eye.
if too black feathers are in g. will need extra or g. tan for back

CHAPTER 3

Tales of a Honey Bear and a Mallard Duck

Paperweight production on the factory floor involves a range of carefully integrated processes connected with the making of the bone-china bodies and their decoration. Before production can begin, however, designers' ideas, worked out in clay and on paper, have to be translated into a form that will ensure that the high standards associated with the range are maintained and that smooth operations in the casting and decorating shops can be guaranteed. These tasks are the responsibility of two departments at Osmaston Road that together form the main bridgehead between the art studios and the production departments. Work carried out in the Mouldmakers Shop and Technical Studio ultimately affects how a new paperweight will look and a new model's fate is largely determined at this point, for, if insurmountable problems are encountered here, the premature death of a new model can occur. This happens only very rarely, however, as the battery of skills in the hands of the technicians who work in these departments is formidable. In this chapter the Old Imari Honey Bear (1996) and the Mallard Duck (1997) have been chosen to illustrate the complex procedures involved in moving a paperweight proposal from the design stage through to the Mouldmakers Shop and Technical Studio and then into general factory production.

MODELLING, MOULDMAKING AND THE PRODUCTION OF PAPERWEIGHT BODIES

The Mallard Duck paperweight, first proposed in 1995, developed the waterbird theme that started with the Duck in 1981. John Ablitt was invited to take responsibility for all aspects of the new model's design. The first stage in the development of the paperweight involved the production of a clay model that would provide the basis for moulds from which bone-china bodies could be cast and fired. Before Ablitt started work, however, he wanted to learn more about the bird's overall appearance and behaviour. Fortuitously, in the spring of 1996 a small family of mallards took up residence in the

opposite
Artwork by John Ablitt for Mallard Duck, introduced 1997

back garden of his house in rural Somerset, so he and his wife, Helen, encouraged the ducks by feeding them every morning, and for several weeks he was able to observe and sketch the birds first hand, record details of shape and feather patterns and make notes about their behaviour. Ablitt's resulting sculpture successfully captured the sleek lines and graceful body of the adult male bird while the gentle inclination of the head exactly mimicked a posture Ablitt had often seen the bird adopt during swimming. Every aspect of the overall body form, including the disposition of the wings and tail feathers, was delicately defined in the clay model, as Ablitt knew that the porcelain bodies produced from his sculpture would exactly replicate the original. Particular attention was paid to the form of the three-dimensional surfaces that would ultimately be decorated with the lithographs developed from his artwork. When, after several weeks' work, the modelling was completed to Ablitt's satisfaction, he packed the model into a plastic sandwich box, placed it on the back seat of his Mini and transported it up to Derby. The clay bird was destined for the factory's Mouldmakers Shop tucked away at the back of the Osmaston Road site.

Rubber mouldmaking and the four-part boxes used to make the Mallard Duck slip-casting boxes

The bone-china bodies of the Mallard Duck paperweights would eventually be made in the factory's casting shops using liquid slip (a mixture of fine clays dissolved in water). The task of the Mould-makers Shop was to design and make the Plaster of Paris box-moulds from which the duck paperweights could be slip-cast. (As these boxes would each produce only about forty porcelain bodies before wearing out, many would be needed to keep the paperweight in continuous production.) In the first stage the Head Mouldmaker, Terry Roberts, appraised the sculpture so as to decide on the form of the box-mould needed to make the Mallard Duck bodies. The complex shape found in the tail area of the original sculpture indicated that a four-part box-mould would be needed to enable the unfired clay birds to emerge cleanly and crisply. After the design of the box-mould had been determined, an exact plaster replica of the original clay sculpture was made. From this model impressions were taken to produce a set of rubber moulds from which the various Plaster of Paris box parts could be manufactured.

Slip casting – pouring liquid slip into a Mallard Duck box

The Plaster of Paris box-moulds destined to produce Mallard Duck paperweight bodies are assembled and bound tightly with tape in the factory casting shop. Every paperweight is produced from a liquid slip generated from a finely balanced mixture of china clay (25%), china stone (25%), both imported from St Austell in Cornwall, and bone ash (50%), imported from Holland, which is then blended with water. The precise recipe for Derby bone china has evolved over a period of many years. It is capable of withstanding the high kiln temperatures required to produce the hard, white, translucent body needed for the paperweights. Liquid slip is poured into each mould through a small hole in the top of the Plaster of Paris box, which is then left for several minutes so casting can take place. The walls of the boxes gradually absorb water from the slip, and a skin of clay, which gradually thickens as time passes, forms round the edge of the moulds to create the bodies of weights. One of the skills of the slip caster lies in his knowledge of how long to leave the boxes before pouring out the excess slip. When this has been poured out, and after drying for a short period, each box-mould is carefully taken apart to expose the clay body of the Mallard Duck paperweight. At this stage the models are still soft, or 'cheese hard' as the slip casters refer to them, so they must be treated delicately.

Splitting a slip-casting box containing a clay Mallard Duck

The technology used to make the Mallard Duck paperweight, and indeed all paperweight bodies, was first introduced into the ceramic industry in the early eighteenth century, and it has been used at the Osmaston Road factory since the late 1870s. It is traditional for making hollowares such as cups, bowls, jugs and tureens, and it was well suited to the manufacture of the paperweight forms when they were introduced in 1981. The technology, however, limits the degree of complexity of shape that can be produced, and this is partly why the original paperweight brief stipulated that the designs should be abstractions of the animals being represented. John Ablitt was always aware of the technological limitations of the slip-casting technique. Nevertheless, his design for the Mallard Duck sculpture shows the level of sophistication that can be achieved with the method when complex box-moulds involving four or more parts are developed. The close working relationship developed between Ablitt and Roberts is typical of the high degree of co-operation that has been achieved between the Art Studio and the Mouldmakers Shop.

Fettling the clay Mallard Duck to remove seam lines

Fettling, an expert job, involves the removal of any seam lines which result from the casting process, and is carried out before the first firing. The models are of course hollow, and the small holes found in the base of each weight make it possible at this stage to pour out the excess slip. In the paperweight range, the holes are an integral part of the structure of the models, allowing owners to add weight by pouring sand into them. Before the weights leave the factory, a simulated-gold stopper is placed in the apertures. Before firing, the holes are measured precisely to ensure that the stoppers will be exactly the right size. After quality checking has taken place and any bodies

Paperweights on a kiln trolley to be wheeled into the kiln

Mallard Ducks before firing

Glazing process

with even a minute flaw have been discarded, the clay bodies are placed on the lower shelves of kiln trolleys along with other holloware items that are awaiting firing. The loaded wagons are then wheeled into the gas-fired kilns. Firing takes twenty-four hours in total – eleven and a half hours building up to the required temperature of 1250° Celsius, two and a half hours at this temperature, then a ten-hour gradual cooling process. On removal from the kilns the bodies have the white, hard and translucent qualities of Derby bone china, but at this point they are still porous and have a matt surface texture. The ware is referred to as 'biscuit' and remains like this until it has been glazed. After firing, the Mallard Duck paperweight bodies are approximately nine tenths the size of the original clay bodies placed in the kiln, the heat of the kiln having caused a loss of moisture which in turn produces the dramatic shrinkage noticeable in the fired items.

After further quality checks have been carried out and any rejected items have been discarded, the bone-china weights are passed on to the glazing shop. They are then placed on moving spikes and sprayed with a solution of water and dissolved frit (ground-up glass), made up to a precise recipe. The weights are then fired again in a glost kiln at a temperature of 1100° Celsius for about an hour, in a firing cycle of approximately twelve hours in all. The firing process causes vitrification to take place and the glaze fuses with the china bodies of the weights. When they emerge from the glost kilns they have a clear, glassy and polished appearance, and after further quality checks they are ready for decorating.

ARTWORK

Designers produce artwork for the paperweights on paper, usually consisting of a sheet that will show two or three views of a weight drawn from different angles. While the drawings are not in any sense to scale, they are highly accurate in terms of the artist's idea of the way the finished weight should look; the artist determines every detail of the lines, patterns and colours he or she wishes to see developed on the body of a new model.

Early in 1996 a decision was taken to produce an Imari version of the Honey Bear paperweight that had been introduced in 1994. As it had been popular with customers there was no need to commission a new clay sculpture, and the mould developed for this bear, which had been modelled by Bob Jefferson, was recycled. Sue Rowe was given the task of designing the graphics for the Imari version of the Bear; she chose to develop a theme based on the 'Old Imari' pattern, or pattern no. 1128 as it is commonly known at the factory. This was a design, based on much earlier Derby Imari patterns, which had been developed in the Art Studio at Osmaston Road in approximately 1880. The original artwork for it is contained in a pattern book that is held in the company's Museum Archive. The artwork consists of a hand-painted segment of a plate design, and provides details of the in-glaze mazarine-blue ground colour and flower-head, the latter to be reserved on a white background, together with the fine detail of the iron-red florets and trailing foliage to be applied on-glaze and of the fine gilt work that would be laid down over most of the pattern. 'Old Imari' has proved to be one of the most popular and enduring of all the Royal Crown Derby Japan patterns and a modified form of it is still very much in production today. The design for the 'Old Imari' Honey Bear would, in Rowe's mind, reflect all the traditions of the old design, but be appropriate for the new paperweight. Her graphic designs for the Old Imari Bear showed him cloaked in an 1128-inspired long-sleeved jacket of dark blue, fastened at the neck, with the back and sleeves incorporating, within reserved areas, 'Old Imari' motifs including flower-heads and Samurai badge-scales, the whole fully enriched with gilt detailing. On the exposed chest of the Bear she developed a complementary design of blue, iron red and gilt

Old Imari Honey bear and corresponding artwork, with an old pattern book showing the 'Old Imari' pattern no. 1128 and a modern plate using the same pattern

45

based on the one found on the reserved area of the original plate design, and iron-red floral motifs were also used to adorn the white areas of the Bear's rear legs. Gilt brushwork provided the facial details of the mouth, nose, eyes and ears and the blue and gilt 'Old Imari' floral skull-cap; finally the detailing on the right hind paw completed the overall design. The 1128 pattern might have looked out of place on the body of a bear, but Sue Rowe has made it look highly appropriate for an indulgent Honey Bear through the clever use of the concept of the colourful, Imari-inspired jacket.

Ablitt's artwork for the Mallard Duck paperweight (see p. 40), completed in the spring of 1996 after the clay sculpture had been developed, showed three views of the duck's feather patterns – a side view revealing all the detail of the head, beak and chest and the disposition of the wings and tail in relation to the rest of the body; a dorsal view depicting the intricate feather patterns found on the back of the bird; and a third view of the detailing of the underside of the tail area. Overall, the artwork reflected a fairly traditional rendering of a male mallard's feather patterns, but, with the exception of the head area, the body colours were inspired by a Derby Imari palette from which Ablitt developed his own individual theory of Derby richness. At the base of the sheet, a series of small boxes of colour provided the Technical Studio and Print Workshop with precise specifications of the colours he wished to see used to develop the surface decoration.

THE TECHNICAL STUDIO

The coloured transfers needed to manufacture Derby products that are not entirely hand-painted are usually made in-house under the supervision of Print Shop Manager Paul Warner. To make a lithographic transfer that can be applied to a bone-china body, a screen-printing method is used whereby layers of colour and gold are laid down on a special paper, one on top of another, with drying stages in between each one, until the final design is complete. As many of the paperweight designs involve in-glaze as well as on-glaze colours, two separate sets of lithographs are needed for each process and they must, of course, register one on top of the other exactly. As paperweight designs have become more intricate in terms of the amount and type of decoration and the range and number of colours used, so the business of making the transfers has become more complex. Densitometers enable the Print Shop to reproduce an artist's colours exactly, and polyester screens with very fine meshes, which have long since replaced silk screens, help in the production of detail, but it is essentially the work that takes place in the Technical Studio that translates an artist's design into a set of screens that will print the final set of lithographs used to decorate a paperweight. As designs have become more complex, so the number of screens needed to produce the lithographs has increased. Up to fifteen or twenty separate screens may be needed to produce the transfers necessary to decorate a particular weight. We shall examine next how the work of the Technical Studio enables the Print Shop to perform its task.

When the artwork for the Honey Bear and the Mallard Duck had been completed it was passed over to the Technical Studio for the conversion work that would enable the Print Shop to produce the lithographs in sufficient quantity to enable the paperweight to go into full-scale factory production. The work that takes place in this studio not only determines the finished look of a weight, but also ensures that the model will pass smoothly through the decorating shops. Designers are aware of the technology used to produce the weights and of the restrictions that are imposed on them by it, but the technicians have, over a period of years, pushed the technology right to its limits in realizing the artists' wishes. It is the symbiotic relationships formed between artists and technicians and the development of skills in this department that have enabled the paperweight range to evolve in the dynamic way that it has over the last nineteen years.

The Technical Studio is on the first floor of the Osmaston Road factory, situated very close to the Art Studio, so there can be a constant dialogue between the staff working in the two areas. Avis Garton, Head of the Studio, has worked for Royal Crown Derby for thirty-one years and she knows the technology used to decorate all of the Derby products inside out. Currently she employs seven technicians, one of whom is her twin sister – it is difficult to believe that between them these two have seventy years of experience of working on Derby designs! All the technicians have undertaken an extensive training of up to five years' duration and all have excellent brushwork skills so they can successfully reproduce the artwork of the original artists. They are highly skilled draftsmen in their own right and are fully trained photographic technicians – an essential requirement for developing the materials needed in the Print Shop. The studio is highly unusual in its approach to technical work as there is no division of labour involved in the processing of paperweight designs. Once a technician is assigned to a particular model by the Head of Studio, that person takes responsibility for all the stages involved in the paperweight's development. This is without doubt a highly significant feature of the design and production process at Royal Crown Derby.

Old Imari Honey Bear: fitting
process in the Technical Studio

What happens to the artwork when it arrives in the Technical Studio and how do the technicians translate the designs into a form that will facilitate factory production? The Old Imari Honey Bear and Mallard Duck were both given to Rita Harris, an experienced technician who has worked on many paperweights in the range. Once bone-china samples for the respective weights had arrived in the Studio, Harris began the process of 'fitting'. For the Honey Bear this meant determining how the artist's design would 'work' on the three-dimensional porcelain body. Decisions had to be taken about exactly how many transfers would be needed to achieve the design and what their actual disposition would be on the surface of the model. The objective was to reduce the design to the smallest total number of transfers possible, without compromising the artist's original intentions, in order to increase efficiency in the Decorating Shop. Another major consideration was the shape of the transfers and the way they would behave when they were laid down on the body of the weight. Large transfers applied over complex curving surfaces will often pucker or split, which leads to major quality problems at the production stage, so the strategy is to come up with a solution that produces a set of transfers that look good when laid down, but that are as easy as possible to apply in the Decorating Shop. Yet another problem concerns the fact that motifs established in two dimensions at the artwork stage distort when they are laid down in transfer form over a curved surface. The studio technician has to solve all of these problems simultaneously at this highly important fitting stage, and experience developed over many years counts for much when the tasks in hand may look insurmountable.

Using pencil work and compasses, Harris gradually established basic ideas for the Old Imari Honey Bear by working directly on to the surface of the glazed paperweight. She decided on a fit involving two sets of transfers, an in-glaze set for the blue and green colours and an on-glaze set for the iron-red and gilt parts of the design. The mazarine blue and green need to be fired in-glaze to achieve the consistency of colour and richness of hue characteristic of Derby designs; this means a separate firing after the glaze firing. For the blue and green colours, nine transfers were needed, for the following areas: one for the back extending upwards to the skull-cap on top of the head; one for the chest area; one each for the right and left forelegs; one each for the right and left hind legs; one for the right paw; and two for the right and left cheeks. Another set, identical in shape and registering perfectly with the first, would be necessary for the on-glaze iron-red and gilt decoration, with additional transfers with gilt only needed for the nose and mouth and two eyebrows, giving a total of twelve on-glaze transfers and twenty-one altogether. At this stage the technician covered the surface of the porcelain bear's body with a sticky substance and attached special printers' tissue over it to determine precisely the shape necessary for each transfer. These tissues were then developed into mock transfers, lacking any decorative detail, so they could be taken down to the decorating shop for trial fitting. When the technician and senior decorator were absolutely satisfied that the shapes of the lithograph transfers were exactly right, Harris moved on to the next stage, which involved interpreting Sue Rowe's artwork in relation to the now fixed shapes of the transfers that would be used to decorate the paperweight.

Developing drawings to make into positives at the drawing board for the back of the Old Imari Honey Bear

This stage involved making precision drawings from the artwork for each of the transfers. To make separate screens for each of the colours that, when printed together, combine to make a lithograph, Paul Warner needed a set of positives on plastic film. In the case of the Old Imari Honey Bear there were four in-glaze colours and eight on-glaze colours, so twelve positive sheets had to be produced, each providing exact graphic details in black of the lines and areas of colour to be printed by a particular screen. Each sheet is prepared from the original design in fine-quality pencil work, which is then finished off in black ink. When this has been done for all the relevant transfers they are laid out on one sheet and this is photographed to produce a contact negative. From the negatives positive contact sheets can then be produced. These are rigorously checked for flaws, and where necessary any pinprick holes or scratches are filled in and new contact positive sheets are made. The technician has also to ensure that the sheets will register accurately one on top of another, for, if they do not, overlapping will occur during printing. When this stage has been completed the sheets are ready to send down to the Print Workshop for trial printing.

In many ways the artwork for the Old Imari Honey Bear, though complex in itself, was relatively straightforward, and few problems were encountered in the Technical Studio – thanks to the limited number of colours making up the design and to the experience of the technician. As time has passed, however, many of the designs have increased in complexity and the number of colours needed to produce a paperweight has multiplied. In 1981 the average number of colours necessary to produce the six original paperweights was three; for the weights introduced in 1995 it was seven and as high as nine in a couple of cases. It has been known for some designs to involve as many as fifteen colours. In all these cases positive contact sheets have to be developed for each and every colour.

The increasing complexity of the paperweight designs is well illustrated by Ablitt's Mallard Duck, which needed nine colours to produce the design. The degree of intricacy involved in the feather patterns found on the wings and back was considerable and involved Rita Harris in many weeks' work. Both in-glaze and on-glaze colours were needed to produce the design, and, although the body area required only small areas of an in-glaze black, the in-glaze transfers had to include details of all the decorative work found on the back. These details were printed using 'soot' so that it would burn off during the in-glaze firing, but enable the decorators to apply the in-glaze transfers in exactly the right position on the body to allow application of the on-glaze transfers on top at a slightly later stage of production.

To develop the subtlety of the feather patterns designed by Ablitt, colour washes were needed as well as solid colours, and the situation was made even more complex owing to the fact that certain colours such as the pinky-red came up against blue in one part of the design and against gold in another, making it impossible to screen-print all of the pinky-red part of the pattern in one go. Individual positives had to be developed for two separate, different applications of the pinky-red colour. The feather designs involved the laying down of seven colours and the production of fifteen separate positives to print the lithographs that would form the decoration found on the main body of the duck.

Ablitt's design for the Mallard Duck's head was faithful to the beautiful feather patterns found on the male bird. A dark-blue ground colour combined with an azure-green was used to reproduce the natural effect of speckling and iridescence found on its head. The problems of reproducing this effect on the porcelain model using lithograph technology were considerable and utilized all the combined skills of the Technical Studio. The head of the Mallard Duck paperweight was small and highly curvaceous and there was no way that a single transfer was going to fold over it without puckering and causing

left to right Five stages in the fitting and production processes for the Mallard Duck

frizzling during firing. A new strategy had to be developed to overcome the problem, otherwise the paperweight would have to be abandoned.

In the end, Rita Harris was able to provide a fit for the head using a combination of four separate in-glaze lithographs. With these she could lay down the blue-green colour requirements of the design, but, as it is impossible to overlap transfers of this type, the white areas between the transfers remained a problem. Traditionally, this type of difficulty has been solved by applying a line of gilding over the join areas, but in this case that would have been inappropriate. Rita therefore experimented with disguising the join areas by developing a further set of on-glaze transfers of the same colours. After a series of tests the results were impressive and the Mallard Duck's head appeared just as the artist intended. In this instance the lithograph technology had been pushed to previously unknown limits, and it is hard to imagine how the problem could have been solved without the long-standing skills and experience of the technicians being applied in a novel way.

Old Imari Honey Bear transfers on the press in the Print Workshop

THE DECORATING SHOP

Once the technical work on the two paperweights had been completed the Print Shop manufactured the stocks of transfers needed to decorate them when they went into production. Transfers were printed on sheets of thick paper with a waxy covering, and the lithographs were gradually built up with the various layers of colour. The 22-carat gold was applied through the appropriate screen as a liquid paste – looking a thick chocolate-brown colour at this stage and giving little indication of the rich effect it would generate after application and firing. Once the printing process was completed the stocks of transfers were placed in the Decorating Shop store until production of the weights began.

The Decorating Shop lies at the heart of the factory and is one of the largest spaces in the factory. The highly skilled decorators and

The application of in-glaze transfers in the Decorating Shop and an Old Imari Honey Bear with in-glaze transfers after firing

Mallard duck: the application of on-glaze transfers

Gilding the line round the base of the Mallard Duck's neck

opposite The completed Mallard Duck and Old Imari Honey Bear

gilders each occupy a small work station that sits alongside a conveyor belt on which completed work can be placed for removal to the kilns or quality-checking areas. When a paperweight goes into production all of the decorators learn to apply the lithographs related to that particular model. Where in-glaze colours have to be applied these are laid down first and the soot detailing helps the decorators apply the transfers in just the right place. The first stage in the decoration of the Old Imari Honey Bear and Mallard Duck paperweights involves the soaking of the transfer sheets in a bath of warm water, so that they can easily be removed, and the bone-china bodies are warmed in an oven beneath the bench. With a skilful hand and eye, the transfers are then applied, one by one, to the china bodies. The fit and disposition of the transfers have to be exactly right, and the decorators soon learn to apply them speedily and efficiently using only a small applicator to smooth out any creases. The transfers have, of course, been printed to a specification related to the size of the bodies that emerge from the biscuit kilns. The transfers will stretch slightly to accommodate a weight marginally above average size, but weights on the small size cannot be accommodated and they are discarded. In a nearby cupboard specimen weights finished to the quality standards expected are stored for reference should a decorator wish to carry out a quick comparison with work being undertaken. When the in-glaze transfers have been applied the weights are placed on the conveyor belt to be fired again, which causes the in-glaze colours to sink into the clear layer of glaze and produce a characteristic rich, even hue.

After the in-glaze colours have been fired, the weights return to the Decorating Shop to have the on-glaze transfers applied in exactly the same way as before. This time the decorator lays them down over the in-glaze colours according to the design specification, and it can take a skilled operative up to twenty minutes to complete this stage. This is followed by a fourth firing at approximately 800° Celsius. How long the paperweights spend in the kiln depends on the colour combinations that are being fired and the amount of gold that has been laid down at this point. Gold is particularly sensitive to heat so it must be fired at exactly the right temperature and for the appropriate amount of time, and by this time it is very expensive to incur high levels of wastage. When weights emerge from the enamelling kilns they are passed to the gilding section of the Decorating Shop. Highly skilled gilders apply, in the case of the Honey Bear paperweights, gold lines to complete the join areas between different parts of the waistcoat, while the Mallard Duck has a gilt line applied to the base of the green part of the neck. At this point the weights are fired

Thorough quality checking

for a fifth and final time at 805° Celsius and when the weights emerge from the kiln they are passed to the burnishers, whose job it is to buff the gold area to develop the rich and lustrous shine characteristic of the completed paperweights.

Finally, the completed paperweights are subjected to rigorous quality checks. Weights that meet the strict criteria are fitted with a simulated gold stopper, which signifies premier quality, and they are then forwarded to the warehouse for despatch to retailers. Weights with major flaws are rejected altogether and those with even the minutest of defects are relegated to a second division, fitted with a simulated silver stopper instead of a gold one and then passed to the factory shop, where they are sold as seconds. The factory shop is the only outlet where seconds are sold all year round.

The production of Royal Crown Derby paperweights involves a highly complex and carefully integrated set of processes that worthily continue the development of ceramic-making in Derby over a period of two hundred and fifty years. The ceramic technologies employed in the factory today are a fascinating amalgam of traditional craft skills combined with industrial methods of production; the resulting paperweights are technically of very high quality and clearly reflect the artistic intentions of the designers in all their integrity. The continued development of the skills employed in the Technical Studio has allowed increasingly complex designs to become production realities, sometimes against the odds, and it is difficult to overestimate the role this department has played in the evolution of the paperweight range. The close working relationships developed between sculptors, artists, technical staff, mouldmakers, printers and production staff within the factory community that is Royal Crown Derby ensure that every customer can enjoy the creative inspiration captured in the original clay sculptures and in the brushstrokes of the original artwork. The hallmarks of the factory's paperweight series – artistry, crafts-manship, stylishness, and a richness that is distinctively Royal Crown Derby – will continue to distinguish the range in the years to come.

CHAPTER 4

Marks and Stoppers

MARKS

The distinguishing mark of Royal Crown Derby is applied to the base of each paperweight as a lithograph at the same time that the on-glaze transfers are applied. The mark consists of a cypher surmounted by a crown surrounded by a continuous circle of upper-case text, which reads in the upper half ROYAL CROWN DERBY and in the lower half ENGLISH BONE CHINA. The mark has its origins in those used by William Duesbury to signify wares made at the Nottingham Road works in Derby from 1775, after George III granted the factory the rare honour of being able to incorporate a crown into the backstamp. The present mark was based on one first used to denote the origin of wares made by the Derby Crown Porcelain Company Limited at Osmaston Road soon after its establishment in 1876, and since that date used in modified forms. A small 'c' enclosed in a circle followed by a date and 'Royal Crown Derby' denotes design copyright for a weight; the date is the year the design was registered, not the date of production. The copyright year thus gives an indication when production of a weight first started. The practice of introducing the name of a paperweight into the backstamp has been adopted for some models, including Armadillo, Bengal Tiger, Bengal Tiger Cub, Nesting Bullfinch, Nesting Chaffinch, Nesting Goldfinch, Lion and Zebra.

Beneath the main mark are Roman numerals that denote the year of production. The practice of marking wares with a cypher mark signifying the year of production was introduced in 1880 and has continued to the present day. Using the key on the right it is possible to date the year of manufacture of a particular paperweight precisely, and thus one is able to tell whether a weight was made in the year it was first introduced or towards the end of its production cycle.

Exclusive paperweights, such as those made for a pre-launch, those that form part of a limited edition, or those made exclusively for sale to Royal Crown Derby Collectors' Guild members, also carry

CYPHER MARKS	
XLIV	1981
XLV	1982
XLVI	1983
XLVII	1984
XLVIII	1985
XLIX	1986
L	1987
LI	1988
LII	1989
LIII	1990
LIV	1991
LV	1992
LVI	1993
LVII	1994
LVIII	1995
LIX	1996
LX	1997
LXI	1998
LXII	1999
MM	2000
MMI	2001
MMII	2002
MMIII	2003
MMIV	2004
MMV	2005
MMVI	2006
MMVII	2007
MMVIII	2008
MMIX	2009
MMX	2010

55

The Royal Crown Derby
stamp found on the base of
the paperweights

marks that signify their special status. Details of these marks are given in Chapter Five.

A number of other marks are found on the base of each weight. A small, in-glaze letter in pale blue or green, for example a letter 'f', indicates the identity of the decorator who applied the in-glaze lithographs. Another lower-case letter, in Derby iron red, indicates the identity of the decorator who applied the on-glaze transfers, and a lower-case letter in gold signifies the identity of a gilder. These marks all relate to quality control procedures.

Paperweights sold through the factory shop as 'seconds' have had the Royal Crown Derby mark to the base scratched through with a sharp instrument, and buyers of second-hand weights should check before purchasing if this has occurred as there is often a big difference in price between weights of first- and second-class quality.

STOPPERS

When the paperweights were first introduced in 1981 they were filled with sand at the factory and a small simulated-gold stopper was inserted in the basal holes after filling. The addition of the sand, however, increased transport costs and infringed Health and Safety legislation, so the practice was discontinued and a small card was inserted in the packaging of each weight telling customers how to add weight to a model should this be required. The practice of adding simulated-gold stoppers was continued.

A few years later the decision was taken to increase the weight of clay in the paperweight bodies in order to make them more robust, and the simulated-gold stoppers were replaced with permanently fixed ceramic bungs, each marked with the Royal Crown Derby cypher. This action proved to be unpopular with collectors and the adding of gold stoppers was resumed; this is still the situation today. Factory seconds are fitted with a simulated-silver stopper to signify their lower status. If a person should write to the factory to request a replacement stopper, only a silver one will be issued. All stoppers are moulded to include a reproduction of the standard Royal Crown Derby backstamp.

CHAPTER 5

The Paperweight Menagerie

This is a catalogue of all paperweights introduced between 1981 and late 2000. It is presented in chronological order and each entry gives details of the weight's modeller and designer, height, date of introduction and price at introduction. An alphabetical index has been included on pages 125–26. Owing to popular demand, the Tropical Fish and Miniature Teddy Bears have been included at the end of the Menagerie.

New information about the paperweight series is regularly added to the Royal Crown Derby website (see p. 120 for details).

The Duck, Owl, Penguin, Quail, Rabbit and Wren were the first six paperweights introduced at the Chatsworth House launch in 1981.

Duck

UPPER MIDDLE ROW, LEFT

Modelled by Robert Jefferson
Decorated by Brian Branscombe

Height: 6.5 cm
Introduced: 1981
Price at introduction: £24.95
Withdrawn: 1997
Price at withdrawal: £54.50

Owl

TOP ROW

Modelled by Robert Jefferson
Decorated by Brian Branscombe

Height: 7 cm
Introduced: 1981
Price at introduction: £24.95
Withdrawn: 1992
Price at withdrawal: £49.95

Penguin

UPPER MIDDLE ROW, RIGHT

Modelled by Robert Jefferson
Decorated by Brian Branscombe

Height: 13.5 cm
Introduced: 1981
Price at introduction: £24.95
Withdrawn: 1992
Price at withdrawal: £49.95

Quail

LOWER MIDDLE ROW, LEFT

Modelled by Robert Jefferson
Decorated by Brian Branscombe

Height: 6.5 cm
Introduced: 1981
Price at introduction: £19.95
Withdrawn: 1991
Price at withdrawal: £45

Rabbit

BOTTOM ROW, RIGHT

Modelled by Robert Jefferson
Decorated by Brian Branscombe

Height: 7.5 cm
Introduced: 1981
Price at introduction: £19.95
Still in production

Wren

BOTTOM ROW, LEFT

Modelled by Robert Jefferson
Decorated by Brian Branscombe

Height: 6.5 cm
Introduced: 1981
Price at introduction: £19.95
Still in production

Fox

BOTTOM ROW, LEFT

Modelled by Robert Jefferson
Decorated by Brian Branscombe

Height: 5.5 cm
Introduced: 1983
Price at introduction: £21.95
Withdrawn: 1987
Price at withdrawal: £28.95

This weight, the first of two foxes in the range, had
blue fur-markings to denote an Arctic Fox. It was
one of the first paperweights to be withdrawn from
the range, along with the Seal and the Hedgehog,
in 1987.

Frog

BOTTOM ROW, RIGHT

Modelled by Robert Jefferson
Decorated by Brian Branscombe

Height: 7.5 cm
Introduced: 1983
Price at introduction: £29.95
Withdrawn: 1997
Price at withdrawal: £75.95

Hedgehog

UPPER MIDDLE ROW, RIGHT

Modelled by Robert Jefferson
Decorated by Brian Branscombe

Height: 5.5 cm
Introduced: 1983
Price at introduction: £26.95
Withdrawn: 1987
Price at withdrawal: £34.50

The Hedgehog weight was one of the first weights,
along with the Fox and the Seal, to be withdrawn
from the range in 1987.

Pheasant

TOP ROW

Modelled by Robert Jefferson
Decorated by Brian Branscombe

Height: 6.5 cm
Introduced: 1983
Price at introduction: £26.95
Withdrawn: 1998
Price at withdrawal: £70

Seal

UPPER MIDDLE ROW, LEFT

Modelled by Robert Jefferson
Decorated by Brian Branscombe

Height: 8 cm
Introduced: 1983
Price at introduction: £29.95
Withdrawn: 1987
Price at withdrawal: £41

The Seal, along with the Fox and the Hedgehog,
was one of the first weights to be withdrawn from
the range in 1987.

Turtle

LOWER MIDDLE ROW

Modelled by Robert Jefferson
Decorated by Brian Branscombe

Height: 5 cm
Introduced: 1983
Price at introduction: £26.95
Withdrawn: 1998
Price at withdrawal: £64

Cat

TOP ROW, RIGHT

Modelled by Robert Jefferson
Decorated by Brian Branscombe

Height: 13.5 cm
Introduced: 1985
Price at introduction: £31
Still in production

Harvest Mouse

LOWER MIDDLE ROW, RIGHT

Modelled by Robert Jefferson
Decorated by Brian Branscombe

Height: 6 cm
Introduced: 1985
Price at introduction: £23.50
Withdrawn: 1994
Price at withdrawal: £39.95

Pig

BOTTOM ROW, RIGHT

Modelled by Robert Jefferson
Decorated by Brian Branscombe

Height: 6.5 cm
Introduced: 1985
Price at introduction: £28.50
Withdrawn: 1991
Price at withdrawal: £45

Snail

BOTTOM ROW, LEFT

Modelled by Robert Jefferson
Decorated by Brian Branscombe

Height: 6.5 cm
Introduced: 1985
Price at introduction: £28.50
Withdrawn: 1991
Price at withdrawal: £45

Badger

LOWER MIDDLE ROW, LEFT

Modelled by Robert Jefferson
Decorated by Brian Branscombe

Height: 7.5 cm
Introduced: 1986
Price at introduction: £41
Withdrawn: 1994
Price at withdrawal: £65

Chipmunk

UPPER MIDDLE ROW, LEFT

Modelled by Robert Jefferson
Decorated by Brian Branscombe

Height: 10.5 cm
Introduced: 1986
Price at introduction: £28.95
Withdrawn: 1997
Price at withdrawal: £44.50

Golden Carp

UPPER MIDDLE ROW, RIGHT

Modelled by Robert Jefferson
Decorated by Brian Branscombe

Height: 10.5 cm
Introduced: 1986
Price at introduction: £49
Withdrawn: 1991
Price at withdrawal: £63

Dolphin

TOP ROW, LEFT

Modelled by Robert Jefferson
Decorated by Brian and June Branscombe

Height: 9.5 cm
Introduced: 1987
Price at introduction: £41
Withdrawn: 1993
Price at withdrawal: £69.95

Walrus

MIDDLE ROW, LEFT

Modelled by Robert Jefferson
Decorated by Brian Branscombe

Height: 10.5 cm
Introduced: 1987
Price at introduction: £41
Withdrawn: 1991
Price at withdrawal: £57

Crab

BOTTOM ROW, RIGHT

Modelled by Robert Jefferson
Decorated by Brian Branscombe

Height: 4 cm
Introduced: 1988
Price at introduction: £43.50
Withdrawn: 1991
Price at withdrawal: £53

Dragon

MIDDLE ROW, RIGHT

Modelled by Robert Jefferson
Decorated by Brian Branscombe

Height: 11 cm
Introduced: 1988
Price at introduction: £55
Withdrawn: 1992
Price at withdrawal: £89.95

Koala

TOP ROW, RIGHT

Modelled by Robert Jefferson
Decorated by Brian Branscombe

Height: 11 cm
Introduced: 1988
Price at introduction: £43.50
Withdrawn: 1993
Price at withdrawal: £69.95

The Koala was introduced, along with the Platypus, to mark the 1988 Australian bicentenary celebrations.

Platypus

TOP ROW, LEFT

Modelled by Robert Jefferson
Decorated by Brian Branscombe

Height: 11.5 cm
Introduced: 1988
Price at introduction: £43.50
Withdrawn: 1992
Price at withdrawal: £67

The Platypus was introduced, along with the Koala paperweight, to mark the 1988 Australian bicentenary celebrations.

Chaffinch

BOTTOM ROW, LEFT

Modelled by Robert Jefferson
Decorated by Jo Ledger

Height: 6.5 cm
Introduced: 1989
Price at introduction: £41
Still in production

Hamster

TOP ROW, MIDDLE

Modelled by Robert Jefferson
Decorated by Jo Ledger

Height: 10.75 cm
Introduced: 1989
Price at introduction: £29.95
Withdrawn: 1992
Price at withdrawal: £37

Ram

TOP ROW, RIGHT

Modelled by Brian and June Branscombe
Decorated by June Branscombe

Height: 14 cm
Introduced: 1989
Price at introduction: £99
Withdrawn: 1993
Price at withdrawal: £119

The local football team is known as the Rams and the Ram weight originated from an idea associated with this source. It was the first of the 'large' paperweights and was originally available only from shops that were members of the Guild of Specialist China and Glass Retailers; it was launched worldwide in 1990.

Robin

TOP ROW, LEFT

Modelled by Robert Jefferson
Decorated by Jo Ledger

Height: 6.5 cm
Introduced: 1989
Price at introduction: £33
Still in production

The Robin continues to be one of the most popular models ever manufactured. The weight was again number one bestseller in 1999.

Snake

BOTTOM ROW, LEFT

Modelled by Robert Jefferson
Decorated by Jo Ledger

Height: 8.25 cm
Introduced: 1989
Price at introduction: £59
Withdrawn: 1991
Price at withdrawal: £63

Baby Rabbit

MIDDLE ROW, RIGHT

Modelled by Robert Tabbenor
Decorated by Brian Branscombe

Height: 4.5 cm
Introduced: 1990
Price at introduction. £29.95
Still in production

Chicken

BOTTOM ROW, RIGHT

Modelled by Robert Jefferson
Decorated by Jo Ledger

Height: 7.5 cm
Introduced: 1990
Price at introduction: £45
Withdrawn: 1998
Price at withdrawal: £58

Crown

MIDDLE ROW, LEFT

Modelled by Robert Jefferson
Decorated by Jo Ledger

Height: 10.5 cm
Introduced: 1990
Price at introduction: £99

The Crown was produced in 1990 to celebrate the centenary of Queen Victoria's grant of the Royal Warrant to the factory in 1890. The weight was available only in 1990 and production ceased at the end of that year. Each weight was accompanied with a certificate.

Ginger Tom

TOP ROW, LEFT

Modelled by Robert Jefferson
Decorated by Brian Branscombe

Height: 13.5 cm
Introduced: 1990
Price at introduction: £45
Withdrawn: 1994
Price at withdrawal: £59.95

Gumps Large Elephant

TOP ROW, RIGHT

Modelled by Robert Tabbenor
Decorated by Jo Ledger

Height: 21 cm
Introduced: 1990
Price at introduction: $1000
Limited edition of 100

This solid gold band version of the large-size Elephant was commissioned by Gumps of San Francisco. The backstamp states: *A Signature Edition for Gumps Limited to 100 This is No.* - and the piece was accompanied by a rolled, beribboned and numbered certificate.

Horse

BOTTOM ROW, MIDDLE

Modelled by Robert Jefferson
Decorated by Jo Ledger

Height: 9.75 cm
Introduced: 1990
Price at introduction: £57
Withdrawn: 1993
Price at withdrawal: £69.95

Produced to coincide with the Chinese Year of the Horse.

Kitten

BOTTOM ROW, LEFT

Modelled by Robert Tabbenor
Decorated by Jo Ledger

Height: 8 cm
Introduced: 1990
Price at introduction: £45
Still in production

Large Elephant

MIDDLE ROW, RIGHT

Modelled by Robert Tabbenor
Decorated by Jo Ledger

Height: 21 cm
Introduced: 1990
Price at introduction: £295
Still in production

Red Fox

BOTTOM ROW, RIGHT

Modelled by Robert Jefferson
Decorated by Brian Branscombe

Height: 5.5 cm
Introduced: 1990
Price at introduction: £33
Withdrawn: 1993
Price at withdrawal: £39.95

The design for this weight was based on the original Fox, sculpted by Jefferson and introduced in 1983. Graphics for the Red Fox were also based on those of the original version.

Small Elephant

MIDDLE ROW, LEFT

Modelled by Robert Tabbenor
Decorated by Jo Ledger

Height: 9.5 cm
Introduced: 1990
Price at introduction: £99
Still in production

Bulldog

UPPER MIDDLE ROW, RIGHT

Modelled by Robert Jefferson
Decorated by Jo Ledger

Height: 9 cm
Introduced: 1991
Price at introduction: £75
Withdrawn: 1997
Price at withdrawal: £82.95

Dormouse

BOTTOM ROW, RIGHT

Modelled by Robert Jefferson
Decorated by Jo Ledger

Height: 5 cm
Introduced: 1991
Price at introduction: £29.95
Withdrawn: 1999
Price at withdrawal: £35

Goldcrest

LOWER MIDDLE ROW, LEFT

Modelled by Robert Jefferson
Decorated by Jo Ledger

Height: 5.5 cm
Introduced: 1991
Price at introduction: £29.95
Still in production

Imari Dormouse

LOWER MIDDLE ROW, RIGHT

Modelled by Robert Jefferson
Decorated by Jo Ledger

Height: 5 cm
Introduced: 1991
Price at introduction: £39
Withdrawn: 1994
Price at withdrawal: £49.95

Russian Bear

TOP ROW

Modelled by Robert Jefferson
Decorated by Jo Ledger

Height: 8.5 cm
Introduced: 1991
Price at introduction: £49.95

This weight was introduced in 1991 but was sold only in Canada. During 1998 this weight was also available to members of the Royal Crown Derby Collectors' Guild before its retirement at the end of that year.

Seahorse

BOTTOM ROW, LEFT

Modelled and decorated
by June Branscombe

Height: 9.75 cm
Introduced: 1991
Price at introduction: £85
Withdrawn: 1994
Price at withdrawal: £99.95

Sheep

UPPER MIDDLE ROW, LEFT

Modelled and decorated
by June Branscombe

Height: 9.75 cm
Introduced: 1991
Price at introduction: £69
Withdrawn: 1995
Price at withdrawal: £75

Sleeping Kitten

BOTTOM ROW, LEFT

Modelled by Robert Tabbenor
Decorated by Jo Ledger

Height: 4.5 cm
Introduced: 1991
Price at introduction: £49
Still in production

Squirrel

UPPER MIDDLE ROW, RIGHT

Modelled by Robert Jefferson
Decorated by Jo Ledger

Height: 8.5 cm
Introduced: 1991
Price at introduction: £49
Withdrawn: 1996
Price at withdrawal: £51.95

Bald Eagle

LOWER MIDDLE ROW, LEFT

Modelled by Robert Jefferson
Decorated by Jo Ledger

Height: 17 cm
Introduced: 1992
Price at introduction: £175
Still in production

A signature edition Bald Eagle was produced for Gumps of San Francisco in 1991. The backstamp stated *A Signature Edition for Gumps Limited to 100 This is No. – Signed by The Hon. Hugh Gibson Managing Director The Royal Crown Derby Porcelain Company Limited*. Each piece was accompanied by a rolled, beribboned and numbered certificate.

Bull

TOP ROW

Modelled by Robert Jefferson
Decorated by Jo Ledger

Height: 13 cm
Introduced: 1992
Price at introduction: £225
Still in production

Cockerel

UPPER MIDDLE ROW, LEFT

Modelled by Robert Jefferson
Decorated by Jo Ledger

Height: 9.25 cm
Introduced: 1992
Price at introduction: £59.95
Withdrawn: 1999
Price at withdrawal: £78

Lamb

BOTTOM ROW, RIGHT

Modelled and decorated
by June Branscombe

Height: 6.5 cm
Introduced: 1992
Price at introduction: £39.95
Withdrawn: 1996
Price at withdrawal: £51.95

Monkey and Baby

LOWER MIDDLE ROW, RIGHT

Modelled by Robert Jefferson
Decorated by Jo Ledger

Height: 10 cm
Introduced: 1992
Price at introduction: £89.95
Withdrawn: 1994
Price at withdrawal: £99.95

Produced to coincide with the Chinese Year of the Monkey.

Humming Bird

LOWER MIDDLE ROW, LEFT

Modelled and decorated by John Ablitt

Height: 10 cm
Introduced: 1993
Price at introduction: £49.95
Withdrawn: 2000
Price at withdrawal: £62

This was John Ablitt's first paperweight design.

King Charles Spaniel

BOTTOM ROW, LEFT

Modelled by Robert Jefferson
Decorated by Jo Ledger

Height: 9.75 cm
Introduced: 1993
Price at introduction: £63
Withdrawn: 1995
Price at withdrawal: £65

Kingfisher

UPPER MIDDLE ROW, LEFT

Modelled by Robert Jefferson
Decorated by Des Martin

Height: 10.5 cm
Introduced: 1993
Price at introduction: £63
Still in production

Playful Kitten

LOWER MIDDLE ROW, RIGHT

Modelled by Robert Tabbenor
Decorated by Jo Ledger

Height: 6.5 cm
Introduced: 1993
Price at introduction: £49.95
Withdrawn: 1996
Price at withdrawal: £55

Tiger Cub

UPPER MIDDLE ROW, RIGHT

Modelled by Robert Jefferson
Decorated by Jo Ledger

Height: 8 cm
Introduced: 1993
Price at introduction: £63
Withdrawn: 1995
Price at withdrawal: £65

Twin Lambs

BOTTOM ROW, RIGHT

Modelled and decorated
by June Branscombe

Height: 4 cm
Introduced: 1993
Price at introduction: £49.95
Withdrawn: 1997
Price at withdrawal: £56.50

Beaver

UPPER MIDDLE ROW, MIDDLE

Modelled by Robert Jefferson
Decorated by Jo Ledger

Height: 7.5 cm
Introduced: 1994
Price at introduction: £49.95
Withdrawn: 1997
Price at withdrawal: £51.50

Bengal Tiger

TOP ROW

Modelled and decorated by John Ablitt

Height: 13 cm
Introduced: 1994
Price at introduction: £165
Withdrawn: 1999
Price at withdrawal: £195

Blue Tit

BOTTOM ROW, RIGHT

Modelled by Robert Jefferson
Decorated by Avis Garton

Height: 7 cm
Introduced: 1994
Price at introduction: £39.95
Still in production

Deer

TOP ROW

Modelled and decorated by John Ablitt

Height: 13.5 cm
Introduced: 1994
Price at introduction: £150
Guild members' exclusive

The Deer paperweight was the first weight to be designed and manufactured as an exclusive for members of the Royal Crown Derby Collectors' Guild. It was no longer available for order after 1994. Each weight bears a special backstamp that states *Designed Exclusively for The Royal Crown Derby Collectors' Guild.*

Honey Bear

MIDDLE ROW, RIGHT

Modelled by Robert Jefferson
Decorated by Jo Ledger

Height: 10.5 cm
Introduced: 1994
Price at introduction: £79.95
Withdrawn: 1997
Price at withdrawal: £82.50

Panda

BOTTOM ROW, LEFT

Modelled by Robert Jefferson
Decorated by Rita Harris

Height: 10 cm
Introduced: 1994
Price at introduction: £69.95
Still in production

Ashbourne Hedgehog

MIDDLE ROW, LEFT

Modelled by Robert Jefferson
Decorated by John Ablitt

Height: 5.5 cm
Introduced: 1995
Price at introduction: £59
Limited edition of 500

This paperweight was produced as an exclusive for the china retailer John Sinclair (now Sinclairs) of Sheffield and Bakewell. It is based on the original Hedgehog paperweight introduced in 1983, modelled by Bob Jefferson, but new graphic designs were developed by John Ablitt. The paperweight carries, in addition to the usual Royal Crown Derby cypher, a mark stating *Made Exclusively for John Sinclair.* The weights do not bear a number, but each paperweight was issued with a numbered certificate.

Bakewell Duck

LOWER MIDDLE ROW, RIGHT

Modelled by Robert Jefferson
Decorated by John Ablitt

Height: 6.5 cm
Introduced: 1995
Price at introduction: £54.95
Limited edition of 500

This paperweight was produced as an exclusive for the china retailer John Sinclair (now Sinclairs) of Sheffield and Bakewell. It is based on the original Duck paperweight introduced in 1981, modelled by Bob Jefferson, but new graphic designs were developed by John Ablitt. The paperweight carries, in addition to the usual Royal Crown Derby cypher, a mark stating *Made Exclusively for John Sinclair*. The weights do not bear a number, but each paperweight was issued with a numbered certificate.

Barn Owl

UPPER MIDDLE ROW, RIGHT

Modelled and decorated by John Ablitt

Height: 11 cm
Introduced: 1995
Price at introduction: £62.95
Still in production

Bengal Tiger Cub

UPPER MIDDLE ROW, LEFT

Modelled and decorated by John Ablitt

Height: 10.5 cm
Introduced: 1995
Price at introduction: £79.95
Withdrawn: 1999
Price at withdrawal: £90

The Bengal Tiger Cub paperweight was pre-launched by the china retailer Bennetts of Derby. The pre-launch issue consisted of a hundred weights, each carrying the usual backstamp, but in gold rather than iron red. General-production weights bear the standard Royal Crown Derby marks.

Blue Jay

TOP ROW

Modelled and decorated by John Ablitt

Height: 9 cm
Introduced: 1995
Price at introduction: £59.95
Withdrawn: 1999
Price at withdrawal: £64

Contented Cat

BOTTOM ROW

Modelled and decorated by John Ablitt

Height: 6 cm
Introduced: 1995
Price at introduction: £59.95
Withdrawn: 1998
Price at withdrawal: £48

Coot

LOWER MIDDLE ROW, LEFT

Modelled and decorated by John Ablitt

Height: 5.5 cm
Introduced: 1995
Price at introduction: £49.95
Withdrawn: 1997
Price at withdrawal: £54.50

Dove

TOP ROW, LEFT

Modelled and decorated
by June Branscombe

Height: 23 cm
Introduced: 1995
Price at introduction: gold edition £430;
others £380
Limited edition of 150

Commissioned by Wheelers of Loughborough, the
Dove paperweight commemorated *50 years of Peace
in Europe 1945–95.* The edition of 150 weights
consisted of a sub-edition of fifty that had a gold
backstamp including the 1945 Royal Crown Derby
mark as well as the 1995 one. All weights in the
limited edition had backstamps that stated *Spirit of
Peace* and *An exclusive edition commissioned by
Wheelers of Loughborough to commemorate the 50th
Anniversary of V.E. Day 1945–1995, No – of 150.*

Grey Kitten

LOWER MIDDLE ROW, LEFT

Modelled by Robert Tabbenor
Decorated by Jo Ledger

Height: 8 cm
Introduced: 1995
*Price at introduction: Complimentary to new Guild
members*

This paperweight was not manufactured after 1995.

Mole

BOTTOM ROW, LEFT

Modelled by Robert Jefferson
Decorated by Sue Rowe

Height: 5 cm
Introduced: 1995
Price at introduction: £45
Guild members' exclusive

The Mole was the Royal Crown Derby Collectors'
Guild piece for 1995 and only available to Guild
members. It was not manufactured after 1995. Each
weight bears a mark that states *An Exclusive for The
Royal Crown Derby Collectors' Guild.*

Waxwing

BOTTOM ROW, RIGHT

Modelled by Robert Jefferson
Decorated by Jo Ledger

Height: 8.5 cm
Introduced: 1995
Price at introduction: £49.95
Withdrawn: 1998
Price at withdrawal: £56

Zebra

UPPER MIDDLE ROW, RIGHT

Modelled and decorated by John Ablitt

Height: 13.5 cm
Introduced: 1995
Price at introduction: £145
Withdrawn: 1998
Price at withdrawal: £160

The Zebra was pre-launched by Harrods in April
1995. The pre-launch edition of one hundred
weights carried a special backstamp that stated *An
Exclusive Signature Edition for Harrods, Signed by the
Artist John Ablitt.* General-production Zebra
weights bear standard Royal Crown Derby marks.

Armadillo

BOTTOM ROW, LEFT

Modelled and decorated by John Ablitt

Height: 8 cm
Introduced: 1996
Price at introduction: £59.95
Withdrawn: 1999
Price at withdrawal: £68

Buxton Badger

MIDDLE ROW, LEFT

Modelled by Robert Jefferson
Decorated by John Ablitt

Height: 7.5 cm
Introduced: 1996
Price at introduction: £65
Limited edition of 500

This paperweight was produced as an exclusive for the china retailer John Sinclair (now Sinclairs) of Sheffield and Bakewell. It is based on the original Badger paperweight introduced in 1986, modelled by Bob Jefferson, but new graphic designs were developed by John Ablitt. The paperweight carries, in addition to the usual Royal Crown Derby cypher, a mark stating *Exclusive to John Sinclair*. The weights do not bear a number, but each paperweight was issued with a numbered certificate.

Camel

TOP ROW

Modelled and decorated by John Ablitt

Height: 17.5 cm
Introduced: 1996
Price at introduction: £245
Still in production

The special edition was introduced in 1996. This carried the Harrods logo on the leg and a special backstamp stating *An Exclusive Signature Edition for Harrods Signed by the Artist John Ablitt*.

Cheshire Cat

MIDDLE ROW, RIGHT

Modelled by Robert Jefferson
Decorated by John Ablitt

Height: 13.5 cm
Introduced: 1996
Price at introduction: £85
Limited edition of 500

This paperweight was produced as an exclusive for the china retailer John Sinclair (now Sinclairs) of Sheffield and Bakewell. It is based on the original Cat paperweight introduced in 1985, modelled by Bob Jefferson, but new graphic designs were developed by John Ablitt. The paperweight carries, in addition to the usual Royal Crown Derby cypher, a mark stating *An Exclusive for John Sinclair*. The weights do not bear a number, but each paperweight was issued with a numbered certificate.

Contented Kitten

BOTTOM ROW, RIGHT

Modelled and decorated by John Ablitt

Height: 4.5 cm
Introduced: 1996
Price at introduction: £45
Withdrawn: 1998
Price at withdrawal: £48

Fawn

BOTTOM ROW, RIGHT

Modelled and decorated by John Ablitt

Height: 14 cm
Introduced: 1996
Price at introduction: £79.95
Guild members' exclusive

Made as a complement to the Deer paperweight, the Fawn was also produced as an exclusive for members of the Royal Crown Derby Collectors' Guild. It was no longer available for order after 1996. The weight has a special backstamp that states *An Exclusive for the Royal Crown Derby Collectors' Guild.*

Lion

TOP ROW

Modelled and decorated by John Ablitt

Height: 14.5 cm
Introduced: 1996
Price at introduction: £199
Withdrawn: 2000
Price at withdrawal: £225

The Lion paperweight was pre-launched by Harrods towards the end of 1996. The pre-launch edition weights carried the Harrods logo on the body and a special backstamp that stated *An Exclusive Signature Edition for Harrods, Signed by the Artist John Ablitt*. General-production Lion weights bear standard Royal Crown Derby marks.

Mulberry Hall Frog

MIDDLE ROW, LEFT

Modelled by Robert Jefferson
Decorated by Sue Rowe

Height: 5.5 cm
Introduced: 1996
Price at introduction: £89.95
Limited edition of 500

Commissioned by Mulberry Hall of York in a limited edition of 500, the weight has a special backstamp that states *A Limited Edition of 500. This is No. –*. In addition to the standard Royal Crown Derby marks, each weight bears a mark that includes a tiny view of the half-timbered Mulberry Hall shop encircled by *Fine China and Crystal Specialists, Mulberry Hall, York.*

Piglet

BOTTOM ROW, LEFT

Modelled by Robert Jefferson
Decorated by Sue Rowe

Height: 5 cm
Introduced: 1996
Price at introduction: £39.95
Withdrawn: 1999
Price at withdrawal: £44

Poppy Mouse

BOTTOM ROW, MIDDLE

Modelled by Robert Jefferson
Decorated by Sue Rowe

Height: 6 cm
Introduced: 1996
Price at introduction: Complimentary to new Guild members

The Poppy Mouse uses Jefferson's model of the Harvest Mouse but with entirely new graphic designs by Sue Rowe. The base of the model is decorated with flora associated with the animal's habitat and includes various grasses, poppies and harebells in shades of dark blue, iron red, pale blue and gold. The weight was selected to be the 1996 complimentary weight given to new members of the Royal Crown Derby Collectors' Guild. It was not manufactured after 1996. The weight has a special backstamp that states *Collectors' Guild Exclusive.*

Puffin

UPPER MIDDLE ROW, LEFT

Modelled and decorated by John Ablitt

Height: 11.5 cm
Introduced: 1996
Price at introduction: £59.95
Still in production

Siamese Cat

UPPER MIDDLE ROW, RIGHT

Modelled by John Ablitt
Decorated by Sue Rowe

Height: 13.5 cm
Introduced: 1996
Price at introduction: £55
Still in production

Siamese Kitten

UPPER MIDDLE ROW, MIDDLE

Modelled by John Ablitt
Decorated by Sue Rowe

Height: 8.5 cm
Introduced: 1996
Price at introduction: £45
Still in production

Swan

TOP ROW

Modelled and decorated by Mark Delf

Height: 9.5 cm
Introduced: 1996
Price at introduction: £69.95
Withdrawn: 1999
Price at withdrawal: £78

Bakewell Duckling

LOWER MIDDLE ROW, LEFT

Modelled and decorated by John Ablitt

Height: 6 cm
Introduced: 1997
Price at introduction: £48

This is a colourway of the Swimming Duckling, introduced in 1998, and bears a special backstamp stating *Exclusive to Sinclairs Bakewell Duckling*. The accompanying certificate advises that the weight is time-limited to the twelve month period 1 April 1998 to 31 March 1999.

Catnip Kitten

LOWER MIDDLE ROW, RIGHT

Modelled by Robert Jefferson
Decorated by Louise Adams

Height: 4.25 cm
Introduced: 1997
Price at introduction: Complimentary to new Guild members

The weight has a special backstamp that states *Collectors' Guild Exclusive*. It was not manufactured after 1997.

Ladybird – Two Spot

BOTTOM ROW

Modelled and decorated by John Ablitt

Height: 3.5 cm
Introduced: 1997
Price at introduction: £34.95
Withdrawn: 1999
Price at withdrawal: £38

Ladybird – Seven Spot

UPPER MIDDLE ROW, RIGHT

Modelled and decorated by John Ablitt

Height: 3.5 cm
Introduced: 1997
Price at introduction: £34.95
Still in production

Majestic Cat

UPPER MIDDLE ROW, LEFT

Modelled by Robert Jefferson
Decorated by Carmen Roome

Height: 13.5 cm
Introduced: 1997
Price at introduction: £89.95
Limited edition of 3500

The Majestic Cat is based on the original Cat, modelled by Robert Jefferson and introduced in 1985, but has new graphic designs developed by Carmen Roome. It is produced in a numbered limited edition of 3500 and is only available for purchase at Royal Crown Derby 'roadshow' events.

Mallard Duck

LOWER MIDDLE ROW, LEFT

Modelled and decorated by John Ablitt

Height: 9 cm
Introduced: 1997
Price at introduction: £69.95
Still in production

Mandarin Duck

LOWER MIDDLE ROW, RIGHT

Modelled and decorated by John Ablitt

Height: 7.25 cm
Introduced: 1997
Price at introduction: £69.95
Still in production

Mulberry Hall Large Elephant

TOP ROW

Modelled by Robert Tabbenor
Decorated by Louise Adams

Height: 21 cm
Introduced: 1997
Price at introduction: £595
Limited edition of 500

Commissioned by Mulberry Hall of York, the Large Elephant has a special backstamp stating *Exclusive to Mulberry Hall Fine China and Crystal Specialists, York Limited Edition of 500 This is No. –*. Each paperweight is individually numbered and accompanied by a numbered certificate.

Nesting Bullfinch

BOTTOM ROW, RIGHT

Modelled and decorated by John Ablitt

Height: 6.5 cm
Introduced: 1997
Price at introduction: £52.95
Withdrawn: 1999
Price at withdrawal: £60

This weight was pre-launched to Bennetts of Derby in 1996 with a gold Royal Crown Derby backstamp *Nesting Bullfinch.*

Nesting Chaffinch

BOTTOM ROW, LEFT

Modelled and decorated by John Ablitt

Height: 7.5 cm
Introduced: 1997
Price at introduction: £52.95
Guild members' exclusive

The Nesting Chaffinch was the Royal Crown Derby Collectors' Guild exclusive for 1997. It was not manufactured after 1997. The weights each have a special backstamp that states *An Exclusive for the Royal Crown Derby Collectors' Guild.*

Nesting Goldfinch

BOTTOM ROW, LEFT

Modelled and decorated by John Ablitt

Height: 6.75 cm
Introduced: 1997
Price at introduction: £52.95
Withdrawn: 1999
Price at withdrawal: £60

Nesting Robin

BOTTOM ROW, RIGHT

Modelled and decorated by John Ablitt

Height: 6.75 cm
Introduced: 1997
Price at introduction: £52.95
Withdrawn: 2000
Price at withdrawal: £62

Old Imari Honey Bear

MIDDLE ROW, LEFT

Modelled by Robert Jefferson
Decorated by Sue Rowe

Height: 10.5 cm
Introduced: 1997
Price at introduction: £89.95
Still in production

This weight uses the model of the Honey Bear, originally sculpted by Jefferson, but the graphic design, based on 'Old Imari' pattern no. 1128, was entirely new and produced by Sue Rowe. The weight was pre-launched by the china retailer Govier's of Sidmouth. The pre-launch edition of 250 weights carried a special backstamp that stated *An Exclusive Signature Edition of 250 for Govier's of Sidmouth – Sue Rowe*. General-production Imari Honey Bear weights bear standard Royal Crown Derby marks.

Regal Goldie Bear

TOP ROW

Modelled and decorated by John Ablitt

Height: 12 cm
Introduced: 1997
Price at introduction: £59.95
Limited edition of 1000

This paperweight was produced exclusively for three Royal Crown Derby stockists, P. J. Hadleys of Preston, H.R. Jackson of Bradford and Potter's Wheel of Ashton-under-Lyne. It is a colourway of the original Teddy Bear. In addition to the usual Royal Crown Derby backstamp the mark also states *The Regal Goldie Bear A Limited Edition of 1000*. The weights are not individually numbered but are accompanied by a numbered certificate.

Rowsley Rabbit

MIDDLE ROW, RIGHT

Modelled by Robert Jefferson
Decorated by Sue Rowe

Height: 7.5 cm
Introduced: 1997
Price at introduction: £58.95
Limited edition of 500

Commissioned by the china retailer Sinclairs, the Rowsley Rabbit is based on the Rabbit paperweight, modelled by Jefferson and introduced in 1981. The new graphic designs were developed by Sue Rowe. The paperweight carries, in addition to the usual Royal Crown Derby cypher, a mark stating *An Exclusive for John Sinclair*. The weights do not bear a number, but each paperweight was issued with a numbered certificate.

Stoney Middleton Squirrel

BOTTOM ROW

Modelled by Robert Jefferson
Decorated by Sue Rowe

Height: 8.5 cm
Introduced: 1997
Price at introduction: £57.95
Limited edition of 500

Commissioned by Sinclairs, the Stoney Middleton Squirrel is based on the Squirrel paperweight, modelled by Jefferson and introduced in 1991. The new design was developed by Sue Rowe. The backstamp states *Stoney Middleton Squirrel An Exclusive for John Sinclair*. The weights are not individually numbered but each weight was issued with a numbered certificate.

Teddy Bear

TOP ROW

Modelled and decorated by John Ablitt

Height: 12 cm
Introduced: 1997
Price at introduction: £59.95
Still in production

The Teddy Bear has continued to be popular since its introduction. During 1999 the weight was the fourth bestseller in the range.

Teddy Bear Red Bow Tie

LOWER MIDDLE ROW, RIGHT

Modelled and decorated by John Ablitt

Height: 12 cm
Introduced: 1997
Price at introduction: £59.95
Limited edition of 950

Produced exclusively for Govier's of Sidmouth, this is based on the original Teddy Bear also introduced in 1997 but has a red bow tie. In addition to the Royal Crown Derby backstamp the mark states *Govier's of Sidmouth Edition of 950 Designed by John Ablitt*. The weights are not individually numbered.

Blue Ladybird

UPPER MIDDLE ROW, RIGHT

Modelled and decorated by John Ablitt

Height: 3.5 cm
Introduced: 1998
Price at introduction: £40
Withdrawn: 2000
Price at withdrawal: £45

Brown Pelican

UPPER MIDDLE ROW, LEFT

Modelled and decorated by John Ablitt

Height: 14 cm
Introduced: 1998
Price at introduction: £70
Still in production

The Brown Pelican was pre-launched by Hadleighs in an edition of 500 marked *1978 – 20th – 1998 Hadleigh* to celebrate their twentieth anniversary. A certificate accompanied the weights.

Debenhams Squirrel

LOWER MIDDLE ROW, LEFT

Modelled by Robert Jefferson
Decorated by John Ablitt

Height: 8.5 cm
Introduced: 1998
Price at introduction: £60

A design complementary to the Red Squirrel, this weight was exclusive to Debenhams until the end of 1999. The backstamp is marked *Debenhams Squirrel* and there is no accompanying certificate.

Debonair Bear

TOP ROW, RIGHT

Modelled and decorated by John Ablitt

Height: 12 cm

Introduced: 1998
Price at introduction: £65
Guild members' exclusive

A new design on the Teddy Bear weight, the Debonair Bear has a backstamp that states *An Exclusive for the Royal Crown Derby Collectors' Guild*. This weight has not been manufactured since 1998.

Derby County Ram

MIDDLE ROW, RIGHT

Modelled and decorated by John Ablitt

Height: 8 cm
Introduced: 1998
Price at introduction: £54

This is a colourway of the Derby Ram commissioned by Derby County Football Club. The backstamp has the Derby County Ram logo with *1998 Royal Crown Derby*. The time-limited certificate includes the Derby County Ram logo and signatures of Hugh Gibson, Managing Director of Royal Crown Derby, and Lionel Pickering, Chairman of Derby County Football Club. This weight has not been manufactured since 1999.

Derby Ram

MIDDLE ROW, LEFT

Modelled and decorated by John Ablitt

Height: 8 cm
Introduced: 1998
Price at introduction: £54

This weight has been available only at the Royal Crown Derby Visitor Centre. Orders were accepted until the end of February 2000.

Derby Wren

BOTTOM ROW, LEFT

Modelled by Robert Jefferson
Decorated by Sue Rowe

Height: 6.5 cm
Introduced: 1998
Price at introduction: Complimentary to new Guild members

The Derby Wren uses the Wren model originally introduced in 1981. It has a special backstamp which states *1997 Royal Crown Derby Collectors' Guild*. This was not manufactured after 1998.

Imperial Panda

TOP ROW, LEFT

Modelled by Robert Jefferson
Decorated by Sue Rowe

Height: 10 cm
Introduced: 1998
Price at introduction: £89
Limited edition of 1000

This is the first in the Endangered Species series commissioned by Sinclairs. The backstamp states *Imperial Panda Endangered Species for Sinclairs*. The weights are not individually numbered but each weight is accompanied by a numbered certificate.

Little Owl

BOTTOM ROW, RIGHT

Modelled and decorated by John Ablitt

Height: 8 cm
Introduced: 1998
Price at introduction: £60
Still in production

A pre-launch signature edition of 1000 was produced for Sinclairs of Sheffield and Bakewell. The backstamp states *An Exclusive Signature Edition Signed by the Artist*, *Sinclairs* and *John Ablitt*. The weights are not individually numbered but each has a numbered certificate.

Mulberry Hall Baby Elephant

TOP ROW

Modelled by Robert Tabbenor
Decorated by Louise Adams

Height: 9.5 cm
Introduced: 1998
Price at introduction: £245
Limited edition of 950

A numbered limited edition which complements the large Elephant introduced in 1997. The backstamp states *Exclusive to Mulberry Hall Fine China and Crystal Specialists, York Limited Edition of 950.* Each piece is accompanied by a certificate.

Old Imari Frog

BOTTOM ROW, RIGHT

Modelled by Robert Jefferson
Decorated by Sue Rowe

Height: 7.5 cm
Introduced: 1998
Price at introduction: £80
Limited edition of 4500

This weight uses Jefferson's model introduced in 1983. The design is based on 'Old Imari' pattern no. 1128 and produced by Sue Rowe. This is a numbered limited edition of 4500 and is available for purchase only at Royal Crown Derby 'roadshow' events.

Old Imari Polar Bear

MIDDLE ROW, LEFT

Modelled by Robert Jefferson
Decorated by Sue Rowe

Height: 10.5 cm
Introduced: 1998
Price at introduction: £94
Withdrawn: 2000
Price at withdrawal: £102

The design is based on 'Old Imari' pattern no. 1128 and produced by Sue Rowe. A pre-launch signature edition of 500 was produced for Govier's of Sidmouth. The Royal Crown Derby mark also states *An Exclusive Signature Edition of 500 for Govier's of Sidmouth* and Sue Rowe's signature. The weights are not numbered but each is accompanied by a numbered certificate.

Penguin and Chick

MIDDLE ROW, RIGHT

Modelled and decorated by John Ablitt

Height: 12.5 cm
Introduced: 1998
Price at introduction: £66
Still in production

Red Squirrel

BOTTOM ROW, LEFT

Modelled by Robert Jefferson
Decorated by John Ablitt

Height: 8.5 cm
Introduced: 1998
Price at introduction: £60
Still in production

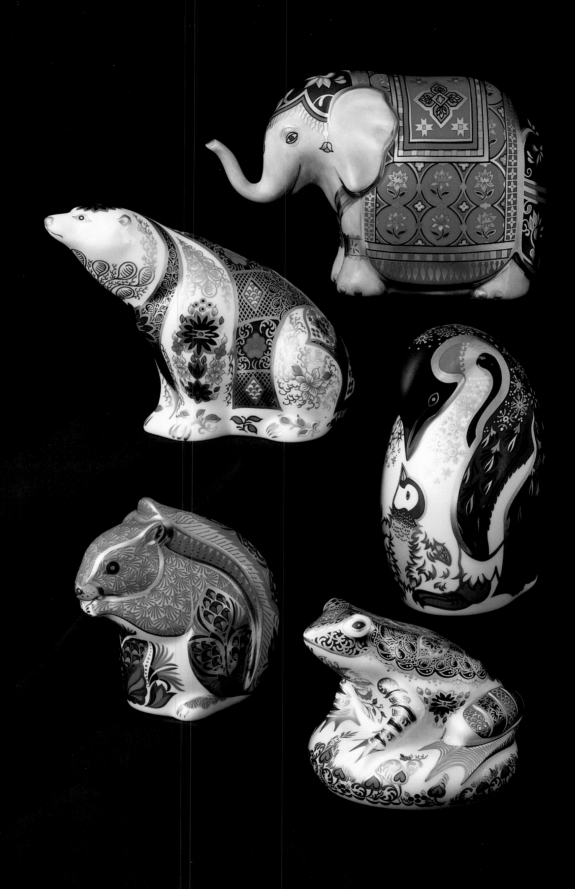

Santa Claus

MIDDLE ROW, RIGHT

Modelled and decorated by John Ablitt

Height: 10 cm
Introduced: 1998
Price at introduction: £59.95
Still in production

Santa Claus was launched in time for Christmas 1997. A Signature Edition Santa Claus was also produced for Lawleys by Post. The signature edition has the usual Royal Crown Derby mark and *Signature Edition of 750 John Ablitt*. These are not individually numbered and are not certificated.

Sitting Duckling

MIDDLE ROW, LEFT

Modelled and decorated by John Ablitt

Height: 7 cm
Introduced: 1998
Price at introduction: £48
Still in production

Swimming Duckling

BOTTOM ROW, LEFT

Modelled and decorated by John Ablitt

Height: 6 cm
Introduced: 1998
Price at introduction: £48
Still in production

Derbyshire Duckling

BOTTOM ROW, RIGHT

Modelled and decorated by John Ablitt

Height: 7 cm
Introduced: 1999
Price at introduction: £48

This is a colourway of the Sitting Duckling exclusive to Sinclairs. Owing to lack of space the backstamp states *Royal Crown Derby* and the certificate advises that the weight is limited to the twelve-month period 1 April 1999 to 31 March 2000.

Dragon of Happiness

TOP ROW, LEFT

Modelled by Mark Delf
Decorated by Sue Rowe

Height: 10 cm
Introduced: 1999
Price at introduction: £175
Limited edition of 1500

The first of two Millennium Dragons, the Dragon of Happiness was commissioned by Peter Jones of Wakefield and the backstamp states *A Pair of Millennium Dragons Dragon No 1: Dragon of Happiness A Limited Edition of 1500 to mark the Millennium Exclusive to Peter Jones China of Wakefield and Leeds*. This is a numbered, limited edition and a numbered certificate accompanies the weight.

Drummer Bear

TOP ROW, RIGHT

Modelled and decorated by John Ablitt

Height: 10.5 cm
Introduced: 1999
Price at introduction: £80
Still in production

The Drummer Bear has proved very popular during its first year of manufacture. The weight was number three in the 1999 sales list.

Drummer Bear for Govier's

TOP ROW, LEFT

Modelled and decorated by John Ablitt

Height: 10.5 cm
Introduced: 1999
Price at introduction: £80
Limited edition of 1500

This version of the Drummer Bear has a drum with a different design. The backstamp states *Drummer Bear An Exclusive Edition of 1500 for Govier's of Sidmouth Designed by John Ablitt.* The weights are not individually numbered but each is issued with a numbered certificate.

Duck-billed Platypus

BOTTOM ROW, RIGHT

Modelled and decorated by John Ablitt

Height: 4 cm
Introduced: 1999
Price at introduction: £65

A time-limited weight from The Australian Collection, launched in advance of the Australian Olympics, the Duck-billed Platypus has a gold signature backstamp and certificate until the end of 2000. From 2001 the weight will have a red backstamp.

Gumps Small Elephant

MIDDLE ROW, RIGHT

Modelled by Robert Tabbenor
Decorated by Jo Ledger

Height: 9.5 cm
Introduced: 1999
Price at introduction: £199
Limited edition of 750

This is a solid gold version of the small Elephant with a special backstamp that includes the Gumps logo and *A Limited Edition of 750.* This is a numbered, limited edition issued with a certificate.

Harrods Large Elephant

TOP ROW, RIGHT

Modelled by Robert Tabbenor
Decorated by Jo Ledger

Height: 21 cm
Introduced: 1999
Price at introduction: £495
Limited edition of 150

This is a colourway of the large Elephant incorporating the Harrods green and the Harrods logo. The backstamp also includes the Harrods logo and this is a numbered limited edition of 150 celebrating 150 years of Harrods.

Kangaroo

BOTTOM ROW, LEFT

Modelled and decorated by John Ablitt

Height: 15 cm
Introduced: 1999
Price at introduction: £125

A time-limited weight from The Australian Collection, launched in advance of the Australian Olympics, the Kangaroo has a gold signature backstamp and certificate until the end of 2000. From 2001 the weight will have a red backstamp.

Koala and Baby

MIDDLE ROW, LEFT

Modelled and decorated by John Ablitt

Height: 9.75 cm
Introduced: 1999
Price at introduction: £90

A time-limited weight from The Australian Collection, launched in advance of the Australian Olympics, the Koala and Baby has a gold signature backstamp and certificate until the end of 2000. From 2001 the weight will have a red backstamp.

Leicestershire Fox

LOWER MIDDLE ROW

Modelled by Robert Jefferson
Decorated by Sue Rowe

Height: 4.5 cm
Introduced: 1999
Price at introduction: £75
Limited edition of 1500

This weight uses the original model by Robert Jefferson introduced in 1983. The named backstamp states *An Edition of 1500 specially commissioned by Wheelers of Loughborough*. The weights are not individually numbered but each is accompanied by a numbered certificate.

Meadow Rabbit

UPPER MIDDLE ROW, RIGHT

Modelled by Robert Jefferson
Decorated by Tien Manh Dinh

Height: 7.5 cm
Introduced: 1999
Price at introduction: Complimentary to new Guild members

This is one of the original six weights, redesigned by Tien Manh Dinh. The backstamp states *An Exclusive for the Royal Crown Derby Collectors' Guild*.

Millennium Bug

BOTTOM ROW, LEFT

Modelled and decorated by John Ablitt

Height: 3 cm
Introduced: 1999
Price at introduction: £45

A new model introduced to celebrate the new millennium, this weight has a named backstamp and an accompanying certificate. This is a time-limited weight, available until the end of 2000.

Millennium Dove

TOP ROW

Modelled by Mark Delf
Decorated by Sue Rowe

Height: 15 cm
Introduced: 1999
Price at introduction: £95
Limited edition of 1500

This special colourway has a backstamp that states *An Exclusive Signature Edition of 1500 for Govier's of Sidmouth*. It includes Sue Rowe's signature and Govier's 2000 pineapple logo. The weights are not individually numbered but each is issued with a numbered certificate.

Nuthatch

BOTTOM ROW, RIGHT

Modelled and decorated by John Ablitt

Height: 5.5 cm
Introduced: 1999
Price at introduction: £56
Still in production

Following the lead of the Robin weight, the Nuthatch was the the second bestseller of 1999.

Partridge

UPPER MIDDLE ROW, LEFT

Modelled and decorated by John Ablitt

Height: 8 cm
Introduced: 1999
Price at introduction: £70
Limited edition of 4500

This weight is a numbered limited edition of 4500 and is available for purchase only at Royal Crown Derby 'roadshow' events.

Rocky Mountain Bear

BOTTOM ROW, LEFT

Modelled by Robert Jefferson
Decorated by Sue Rowe

Height: 8.5 cm
Introduced: 1999
Price at introduction: £94
Still in production

This weight was pre-launched by Govier's of
Sidmouth with the backstamp *Rocky Mountain
Bear An Exclusive Signature Edition of 500 for
Govier's of Sidmouth.* These weights are not
individually numbered but each is issued with a
numbered certificate.

Santa and Sleigh

BOTTOM ROW, RIGHT

Modelled and decorated by John Ablitt

Height: 9.5 cm
Introduced: 1999
Price at introduction: £90
Still in production

Savannah Leopard

TOP ROW

Modelled and decorated by John Ablitt

Height: 13.5 cm
Introduced: 1999
Price at introduction: £195
Limited edition of 1000

This is the second weight in the Endangered
Species series exclusive to Sinclairs. The backstamp
is marked *Savannah Leopard Endangered Species for
Sinclairs.* The weights are not individually numbered
but each is issued with a numbered certificate.

Sitting Piglet

LOWER MIDDLE ROW, RIGHT

Modelled and decorated by John Ablitt

Height: 6.5 cm
Introduced: 1999
Price at introduction: £42
Still in production

Sleeping Piglet

UPPER MIDDLE ROW, RIGHT

Modelled and decorated by John Ablitt

Height: 3.5 cm
Introduced: 1999
Price at introduction: £42
Still in production

Unicorn

UPPER MIDDLE ROW, LEFT

Modelled by Mark Delf
Decorated by Louise Adams

Height: 13 cm
Introduced: 1999
Price at introduction: £180
Limited edition of 2000

This numbered limited edition is available exclu-
sively from the following stockists: Govier's of
Sidmouth, England; Rob McIntosh China, Canada;
Hummel Gift Shop, USA; David Jones, Australia.
The backstamp is marked *Unicorn Specially Designed
to Celebrate the New Millennium by Louise Adams A
Limited Edition of 2000.* Each weight is issued with
a certificate.

Woodland Pheasant

LOWER MIDDLE ROW, LEFT

Modelled by Robert Jefferson
Decorated by Louise Adams

Height: 6.5 cm
Introduced: 1999
Price at introduction: £78
Guild members' exclusive

A new design on the Pheasant paperweight, the Woodland Pheasant has a backstamp that states *An Exclusive for the Royal Crown Derby Collectors' Guild.* This has not been manufactured since 1999.

Baby Rowsley Rabbit

LOWER MIDDLE ROW, RIGHT

Modelled by Robert Tabbenor
Decorated by Sue Rowe

Height: 4.5 cm
Introduced: 2000
Price at introduction: £42

This is an exclusive weight commissioned by Sinclairs. The backstamp is marked *Baby Rowsley Rabbit Exclusive for Sinclairs* and the accompanying certificate advises that the time-limited weight is available from 1 April 2000 to 31 March 2001.

Bluebird

UPPER MIDDLE ROW, LEFT

Modelled by Robert Jefferson
Decorated by Sue Rowe

Height: 6 cm
Introduced: 2000
Price at introduction £75

This weight was pre-launched by Geoff Taylor of Reigate to celebrate their 25th anniversary. It does not have a special backstamp, but does include a certificate.

Computer Mouse

BOTTOM ROW, LEFT

Modelled by Mark Delf
Decorated by June Branscombe

Height: 3 cm
Introduced: 2000
Price at Introduction: £65

Country Mouse

BOTTOM ROW, RIGHT

Modelled and decorated by John Ablitt

Height: 3.5 cm
Introduced: 2000
Price at introduction: £48

Dappled Quail

UPPER MIDDLE ROW, RIGHT

Modelled by Robert Jefferson
Decorated by Louise Adams

Height: 6.5 cm
Introduced: 2000
Price at introduction: £78

Donkey

TOP ROW

Modelled and decorated by John Ablitt

Height: 12 cm
Introduced: 2000
Price at introduction: £95

A signature edition of 1500 will be pre-launched by Govier's of Sidmouth. Weights will have special backstamps and certificates.

Firecrest

BOTTOM ROW, LEFT

Modelled by Robert Jefferson
Decorated by Sue Rowe

Height: 5.5 cm
Introduced: 2000
Price at introduction: Complimentary to new Guild
members

This complimentary weight has a backstamp that
states *Royal Crown Derby Collectors' Guild Firecrest.*
It will no longer be available for order after 2000.

Garden Snail

BOTTOM ROW, RIGHT

Modelled by Robert Jefferson
Decorated by Tien Manh Dinh

Height: 6.5 cm
Introduced: 2000
Price at introduction: £90
Limited edition of 4500

This is a new design using Robert Jefferson's model
introduced in 1985. It is a numbered limited edition
of 4500 and is available for purchase only at Royal
Crown Derby 'roadshow' events.

Ginger Kitten

MIDDLE ROW, RIGHT

Modelled by Robert Tabbenor
Decorated by Jo Ledger

Height: 8 cm
Introduced: 2000
Price at introduction: £56

A colourway of the Kitten produced exclusively for
stockists in the Guild of Specialist China and Glass
Retailers. These 1500 weights do not have special
backstamps but each is accompanied by a certificate.

Golden Pheasant

TOP ROW

Modelled and decorated by John Ablitt

Height: 17.5 cm
Introduced: 2000
Price at introduction: £595

The second of the pair of pheasants produced to
celebrate the 250th anniversary of china manufacture in Derby in 2000. The Golden Pheasant has a
signature backstamp and time-limited certificate
until the end of 2000. From 2001 these weights will
have a red backstamp.

Harrods Bald Eagle

MIDDLE ROW, LEFT

Modelled by Robert Jefferson
Decorated by Jo Ledger

Height: 17 cm
Introduced 2000
Price at introduction: £250

This is a numbered limited edition of 300 and the
design incorporates Harrods green. Each piece will
be accompanied by a numbered certificate.

Heraldic Crown

MIDDLE ROW, MIDDLE

Modelled by Tony Plant
Decorated by June Branscombe

Height: 10 cm
Introduced: 2000
Price at introduction: £195

This is a numbered limited edition of 1000, commissioned by Govier's of Sidmouth to celebrate the
100th birthday of Her Majesty Queen Elizabeth the
Queen Mother. Each piece is accompanied by a
numbered certificate

Lady Amherst Pheasant

TOP ROW

Modelled and decorated by John Ablitt

Height: 17.5 cm
Introduced: 2000
Price at introduction: £595

The first of a pair of Pheasants produced to celebrate the 250th anniversary of china manufacture in Derby in 2000. The Lady Amherst Pheasant has a signature backstamp and time-limited certificate until the end of 2000. From 2001 these weights will have a red backstamp.

Madagascan Tortoise

LOWER MIDDLE ROW, LEFT

Modelled by Robert Jefferson
Decorated by Brian Branscombe

Height: 5 cm
Introduced: 2000
Price at introduction: £75
Limited edition of 1000

This is the third weight in the Endangered Species series commissioned by Sinclairs. The backstamp states *Madagascan Tortoise Endangered Species for Sinclairs.* Each piece is accompanied by a numbered certificate.

Nanny Goat

UPPER MIDDLE ROW, LEFT

Modelled by Mark Delf
Decorated by Tien Manh Dinh

Height: 11 cm
Introduced: 2000
Price at introduction: £85

An exclusive weight available only from the Royal Crown Derby Visitor Centre, the Nanny Goat has a special backstamp stating *Nanny Goat Exclusively availabe from the Royal Crown Derby Visitor Centre.* These weights are certificated.

Orchard Hedgehog

BOTTOM ROW, LEFT

Modelled and decorated by John Ablitt

Height: 5 cm
Introduced: 2000
Price at introduction: £64
Guild members' exclusive

This new model has a backstamp that states *An exclusive for The Royal Crown Derby Collectors' Guild.* This will not be available for order after the end of 2000.

Striped Dolphin

BOTTOM ROW, RIGHT

Modelled by Robert Jefferson
Decorated by Sue Rowe

Height: 9.5 cm
Introduced: 2000
Price at introduction: £90

A pre-launch edition of 1500 with backstamp *The Striped Dolphin A Gold Signature Edition of 1500 Specially Commissioned by Connaught House Sue Rowe.* The weights are not individually numbered but each is accompanied by a numbered certificate.

Turtle Dove

UPPER MIDDLE ROW, RIGHT

Modelled by Mark Delf
Decorated by Sue Rowe

Height: 10 cm
Introduced: 2000
Price at introduction: £99

Posie Paperweights

From 1991 selected paperweights have been
produced, in small numbers, in 'Posie' versions
alongside the standard models. These weights
are characterized by white, clear-glazed bodies
decorated with traditional Royal Crown Derby
'Posie' pattern lithographs, and they bear standard
Royal Crown Derby marks.
Models that include this variation are:
Dragon, Polar Bear, Golden Carp, Quail, Hamster,
Snake, Penguin, Pig, Platypus, Owl.
Production of all 'Posie' paperweights ceased in
1997.

Posie Spaniel

Modelled by Robert Jefferson

Height: 9.75 cm
Introduced: 1997
Price at introduction: £29.95
Limited edition of 1500

This weight uses the model of the King Charles
Spaniel which was modelled by Robert Jefferson
and originally introduced in 1993. Commissioned by
Edwards of Derby as the last 'Posie' Paperweight to
be produced, the Spaniel has the Royal Crown
Derby mark and an inscription stating *Posie
Paperweights 1991–1997 The Spaniel Limited Edition
of 1500*. The weights do not bear a number but each
paperweight is issued with a numbered certificate.

Royal Crown Derby have always considered the Tropical Fish to be a separate collection to the Paperweights and so they were not included in the first edition of the Paperweights book. However, in response to popular demand, we now include full information on these models for collectors who wish to consider them as Paperweights.

Angel Fish

MIDDLE ROW, RIGHT

Modelled by Robert Jefferson
Decorated by Jo Ledger

Height: 11.5 cm
Introduced: 1990
Price at introduction: £57
Withdrawn: 1995
Price at withdrawal: £69.95

Gourami

MIDDLE ROW, LEFT

Modelled by Robert Jefferson
Decorated by Jo Ledger

Height: 11 cm
Introduced: 1990
Price at introduction: £57
Withdrawn: 1995
Price at withdrawal: £69.95

Guppy

TOP ROW, LEFT

Modelled by Robert Jefferson
Decorated by Jo Ledger

Height: 12.5 cm
Introduced: 1990
Price at introduction: £57
Withdrawn: 1995
Price at withdrawal: £69.95

Sweetlips

BOTTOM ROW, RIGHT

Modelled by Robert Jefferson
Decorated by Jo Ledger

Height: 8 cm
Introduced: 1990
Price at introduction: £57
Withdrawn: 1995
Price at withdrawal: £69.95

Koran

BOTTOM ROW, LEFT

Modelled by Robert Jefferson
Decorated by Jo Ledger

Height: 10.5 cm
Introduced: 1991
Price at introduction: £65
Withdrawn: 1995
Price at withdrawal: £69.95

Chevroned Butterfly Fish

TOP ROW, RIGHT

Modelled by Robert Jefferson
Decorated by Jo Ledger

Height: 11 cm
Introduced: 1991
Price at introduction: £65
Withdrawn: 1995
Price at withdrawal: £69.95

The Miniature Teddy Bears form part of the Miniatures range, but as many paperweight collectors have added these to their collections it has been decided that information on each teddy bear should be included in this edition.

Teddy Bear Edward

UPPER MIDDLE ROW

Modelled by Mark Delf
Decorated by Louise Adams

Height: 6.5 cm
Introduced: 1997
Price at introduction: £36

Teddy Bear Victoria

MIDDLE ROW, RIGHT

Modelled by Mark Delf
Decorated by Louise Adams

Height: 7 cm
Introduced 1997
Price at introduction £36

Teddy Bear Alice

MIDDLE ROW, LEFT

Modelled by Mark Delf
Decorated by Louise Adams

Height: 7 cm
Introduced: 1999
Price at introduction: £37

Teddy Bear William

LOWER MIDDLE ROW

Modelled by Mark Delf
Decorated by Louise Adams

Height: 6.5 cm
Introduced: 1999
Price at introduction: £37

Teddy Bears Emma and James

BOTTOM ROW, LEFT AND RIGHT

Modelled by Mark Delf
Decorated by Louise Adams

Height: 6.5 cm and 7 cm
Introduced: 1999
Price at introduction: £80

Emma and James were available as a boxed set. Each pair was certificated as being 'one of an edition exclusively produced for Royal Doulton Retail Divison and available until the end of 1999'.

Daddy and George

TOP ROW, LEFT

Modelled by Mark Delf
Decorated by Louise Adams

Height: 9.5 cm
Introduced: 2000
Price at introduction: £58

Mummy and Charlotte

TOP ROW, RIGHT

Modelled by Mark Delf
Decorated by Louise Adams

Height: 7 cm
Introduced: 2000
Price at introduction: £58

Acknowledgements

Between October 1996 and February 1997 I spent many days at the Royal Crown Derby factory. Many individuals provided information, advice and assistance, and sincere thanks are expressed to all concerned, in particular:

At Royal Crown Derby: The Hon. Hugh Gibson, *Chief Executive*; Simon Willis, *Sales and Marketing Director*; Jo Ledger, *former Art Director*; John Bate, *former Executive-in-Charge*; Sue Morecroft, *Product Manager*; Margaret Sargeant, *Museum Curator*; Louise Adams, *Art Director*; Sue Rowe, *Senior Designer*; John Ablitt, *Designer*; June Branscombe, *Designer*; Avis Garton, *Head of Technical Studio*; May Bottrill, *Design Technician*; Rita Harris, *Design Technician*; Carmen Roome, *Design Technician*; Terry Roberts, *former Head Mouldmaker*; Chris Bottrill, *Clay to Glost Manager*; Martin Hope, *Clay to Biscuit Manager*; Don Fletcher, *former Glost Manager*; Richard Birkin, *Decorating Shop Manager*; Paul Warner, *Print Shop Manager*; Carol Howett, *Lithography Supervisor*; Elizabeth Parr, *Tours Organizer*

At Royal Doulton: Ann Linscott, *former Director of Corporate Communications*; Joan Jones, *Royal Doulton Curator*; Robert Tabbenor, *Modeller*

Special thanks are owed to Glasgow University and to Anneke Bambery, *Principal Curator, Derby Museum and Art Gallery*.

IAN COX 1997

250th Anniversary Edition

Thanks to the following people who have contributed their time and expertise to the revision of this book:

At Royal Crown Derby: Hugh Gibson, *Chief Executive*; Simon Willis, *Sales and Marketing Director*; Stella Birks, *General Manager, Visitor Centre*; Elizabeth Parr, *Tours Organizer*; Heather Poucher, *Product Manager*; Lisa Roberts, *secretary to the Sales and Marketing Director*; and Sally Woodward, *secretary to the Chief Executive*

At Merrell Publishers: Hugh Merrell, Julian Honer, Kate Ward and Matt Hervey
At Nigel Taylor Photography: Mark Duckett

SUE MORECROFT 2000

Further Information

The Royal Crown Derby Collectors' Guild was established in 1994 to enable the company to develop closer relationships with collectors. Membership benefits include:

- An exclusive complimentary paperweight on payment of the annual subscription fee.

- Subscription includes a quarterly magazine, which regularly includes articles and information about Royal Crown Derby products including paperweights.

- Exclusive Club offers, available to members only. Guild exclusives are available only from Royal Crown Derby stockists on production of membership cards.

- Notification of special Royal Crown Derby events.

- A free tour of the Visitor Centre and the Royal Crown Derby factory.

- A free historical enquiry service.

Further details and application forms are available from:
Collectors' Guild, Royal Crown Derby, 194 Osmaston Road, Derby DE23 8JZ, England. It is also possible to enrol as a Guild member at any Royal Crown Derby stockist.

- UK Branch: Royal Crown Derby, 194 Osmaston Road, Derby DE23 8JZ

- US Branch: PO BOX 6705, Somerset NJ 08873

- Canadian Branch: 850 Progress Avenue, Scarborough, Ontario, M1H 3C4

- Australian Branch: PO BOX 47, 17–23 Merriwa Street, Gordon, NSW 2072

- New Zealand Branch: PO BOX 2059, Auckland

The Royal Crown Derby website was created in 1996 to provide new opportunities for the company to develop contacts with customers and collectors. The web pages include a short history of the company and its antecedents, details for those wishing to visit the company in Derby, details of the Royal Crown Derby Collectors' Guild and information about the Royal Crown Derby paperweight range, including lists of stockists. Many of the paperweights are illustrated in colour, and information about new introductions and the latest withdrawals is also given.

Customers and collectors may e-mail the company for further information, or even to suggest new additions to the paperweight range. An Internet discussion forum has also been established.

Royal Crown Derby's website can be visited at the following address: www.royal-crown-derby.co.uk.

VISITING ROYAL CROWN DERBY

Royal Crown Derby has been welcoming visitors to the factory for well over one hundred years. The popular factory tour has recently been enhanced by the new Visitor Centre, which was officially opened by HRH The Princess Anne on 17 February 1999, when a decorated ceramic plaque was unveiled to commemorate the occasion.

The Visitor Centre incorporates the Demonstration Studio, Museum, Factory Shop and the Duesbury Restaurant. Opening times are: Monday to Saturday 9.30 am to 5.00 pm and Sunday 10.00 am to 5.00 pm. Booking for the Visitor Centre is necessary only for groups of twenty or more persons. For further information contact the Tours Organizer on 01332 712800 or 01332 712841.

The Factory Tour

Visitors may tour the working factory accompanied by an experienced guide who explains the processes involved in the production of Royal Crown Derby china tableware and giftware. From claymaking through to burnishing, the details of china manufacture and decoration are revealed. Traditional skills are employed today alongside modern technology. Selection stages throughout the manufacturing process ensure Royal Crown Derby's reputation for quality. Tours last about 70 minutes and take place on Mondays to Thursdays at 10.30 am and 1.45 pm, and on Fridays at 10.30 am and 1.15 pm. Tours may be available by arrangement on some Saturday mornings. Owing to their popularity it is advisable to book in advance.

The Demonstration Studio

Flower-making, fettling, lithographing, gilding and burnishing are all skills demonstrated or explained in the Demonstration Studio. This area allows visitors a closer inspection of the principal skills of china manufacture and decoration, and provides an opportunity to attempt the skills for themselves. The Demonstration Studio is fully accessible to disabled visitors.

The Museum

The factory museum houses a fine collection of Derby porcelain, including pieces made at the Nottingham Road factory between 1750 and 1848, the King Street factory between 1848 and 1935, and the factory at Osmaston Road between the start of production in 1878 and the present day. The cabinet displays are housed in a fine gallery on the first floor of the factory and are augmented by the Ronald Raven Room. A celebrated cancer surgeon and Derby collector, Mr Raven bequeathed his magnificent collection of Derby porcelain of all periods to Royal Crown Derby. It is now displayed in a careful reconstruction of Mr Raven's drawing-room that includes original furnishings and pictures.

The Factory Shop

The extensive factory shop incorporates cabinets displaying best-quality tableware and giftware along with seconds of quality products from all ranges, subject to availability. An exclusive time-limited paperweight and a variety of souvenirs, cards and giftwraps are vailable from the Royal Crown Derby Visitor Centre. Regularly arranged special events offer the chance to purchase other limited-edition pieces.

The factory shop is the only retail outlet selling second-quality paperweights all year round. Customers should check availability before travelling to Derby. Credit-card sales are also available over the phone. The factory shop may be contacted on 01332 712833.

The Duesbury Restaurant

Conveniently situated adjacent to the factory shop is the spacious, architect-designed Duesbury Restaurant. This is a fully licensed restaurant with seating for 120 persons. A range of snacks and meals are served on Royal Crown Derby china. The restaurant is available for private hire for banquets, functions and meetings.

Further Reading

The Story of Royal Crown Derby
John Twitchett, FRSA
Published by Royal Doulton, 1976

Royal Crown Derby
John Twitchett, FRSA
Published by Antique and Collectors' Club, 3rd edition, 1988

*"A Case of Fine China" – The Story of the Founding of
Royal Crown Derby 1875–1890*
Hugh Gibson, Managing Director, Royal Crown Derby
Published by Royal Crown Derby Porcelain Company, 1993
Available from the Royal Crown Derby Museum

Derby China through Three Centuries
Myra Challand, 1991
Available from the Royal Crown Derby Museum

Royal Crown Derby Imari Wares
Ian Cox
Published by Royal Crown Derby Porcelain Company, 1998
Available from the Royal Crown Derby Museum

Royal Crown Derby
Margaret Sergeant
Published by Shire Publications, 2000
Available from the Royal Crown Derby Museum

ROYAL CROWN DERBY

194 Osmaston Road, Derby DE23 8JZ.
Telephone: 01332 712800
Fax: 01332 712899
www.royal-crown-derby.co.uk

DERBY LLAMA

John Ablitt.

June 2000

Index